CHINA AND CUT GLASS

China and Cut Glass

Limoges, Dresden, Bavarian, Austrian Imperial Crown, and Cauldon china; Bohemian and gold glass; vases, Dutch pottery, Dresden clocks, cameo vases and plaques, steins, jardinieres

---

HIGGINS & SEITER
1899

Illustrated Catalog and Historical Introduction

AMERICAN HISTORICAL CATALOG COLLECTION

THE PYNE PRESS

Princeton

First edition

Library of Congress Catalog Card Number 76-162358

ISBN 0-87861-011-1

Printed in the United States of America

Note to the reader. Reproduction of copy and line drawings is as faithful to the original as is technically possible. Broken type and lines which are uneven or broken can be spotted; these are original!

Some individual pages, including those with color plates, have been rearranged.

Higgins & Seiter
Fine China
Rich Cut Glass
New York

ONE ENTRANCE TO STORE

OUR BUSINESS POLICY

Its Results and Prospects

IN issuing this, our Eleventh Annual Catalogue, we beg leave to express to our many customers a hearty appreciation of their former favors, together with the assurance of our utmost endeavor to continue to serve them to the best of our ability as dealers in Fine China and Rich Cut Glass.

Permit us also at this time to call attention to the suggestive fact that from small beginnings we have in a little more than a decade, in addition to our important city and vicinity trade, reached the distinction of doing what is probably the largest mail order business in Glass and China of any house in the United States.

Gratifying as is the record, we should not allude to it here were it not that progress like this means something. More eloquent than words, more convincing than argument, it proves that the principles on which we conduct this business are correct.

We believe, for instance, that customers living at a distance are as quick to appreciate what is latest and most desirable in our wares, as anybody. We see that they get it.

We believe that, as a rule, people whose refinement of taste leads them to desire such goods as we sell, are quick to respond to courteous treatment and fair dealing. We act accordingly.

OUR BUSINESS POLICY—Continued

No matter how remote they live, if reached by freight or express lines, we place at their disposal the combined products of the Glass and China manufactories of the world, in variety beyond precedent or competition.

All goods are sold with the guarantee of safe delivery, and with the right of exchange, or return, if not entirely satisfactory.

Finally, in pursuance of our original price policy adopted after mature deliberation, and maintained with conspicuous success, our goods are uniformly sold on an average, at least,

"One Quarter Less than Elsewhere,"

It is upon these lines, therefore,

The most desirable goods,
In the largest variety,
At 25 per cent. less than usual prices,
With guarantee of satisfaction,
And courteous treatment, always,

that our business has assumed its present magnitude; and it is also upon these lines that we solicit further orders, and anticipate still greater and more pronounced success.

OUR ELEVENTH ANNUAL CATALOGUE

IT IS, we think, with pardonable pride, that we allude to this issue of our Annual Catalogue as the largest and handsomest that we have ever published.

In a measure it keeps step with the progress of the house. To thousands of customers scattered all over the United States it is our only representative. Naturally it is our desire to have it as complete as practicable, and the large expense it entails is neither stinted nor begrudged. We are glad, as always, to send it free to any one who is now, or is likely to be, interested in Fine China and Rich Cut Glass to the extent of being a probable purchaser, because it enables them with actually less inconvenience than is caused by visiting a store in their own vicinity, to order direct from the largest, latest and best chosen assortment in the United States, at prices

"One Quarter Less than Elsewhere."

We are in almost daily receipt of letters expressing appreciation of this opportunity, thanking us for the catalogue, and in many instances asking us to send a copy to some friend. This we are always pleased to do, for we have found that whether "trade follows the flag" or not, trade follows the Catalogue—one order leading to another and another and another, as our goods, prices, and ways of doing business are understood.

A WORD OR TWO ABOUT CUT GLASS

IF THERE were any longer anywhere a doubt as to the supremacy of American Cut Glass, a personal inspection of what in this line we have for sale would dispel it forever. Nothing more brilliant, or in any way more beautiful, has ever been produced than the goods we show. Even the precious metals themselves do not, for table or sideboard purposes, compare in charm with Glass when honestly and artistically produced.

Of course we are not speaking of the cheap "processed," or pressed glass sold elsewhere for a song. Our cut glass is all hand cut—each piece and every line showing the assiduous care, involving in some instances the labor of days and weeks, and which alone gives to Cut Glass its real beauty and intrinsic value.

It may interest some of our customers, who have not already seen the fact noted in the newspapers, to know that when the United States Ambassador to Russia recently laid a wager with one of his St. Petersburg entertainers, that in Cut Glass the United States eclipsed the world, it was to Higgins & Seiter he cabled his order for proof of the truth of his assertion, and that on receipt of the goods, the Russian nobleman paid the bet without argument or a moment's hesitation.

THE CARE OF CUT GLASS

An authority says that glassware will last longer and look better if the following hints as to its care and preservation are regarded. Tepid water, the best Castile or other pure soap, and a stiff brush are the first essentials. After washing and rinsing place the cut glass in boxwood sawdust. This will absorb the moisture in the cutting. Next remove the sawdust from the plain surfaces with a soft cloth. By following these directions the original clearness and sparkle of the glass will be maintained.

Shot should not be used in carafes, cruets, toilet and similar articles. It is very apt to scratch the glass, and thus mar its beauty. Prosaic potato peelings are the best aids. Let them remain in the glassware over night, and then rinse out with a little tepid water.

A very important point is to avoid sudden changes from extreme heat to extreme cold, and vice versa. A pitcher or tumbler which has been filled with ice water, a tray that has been used for ice cream, if plunged at once into hot water will be apt to crack. Use tepid water, and the risk of breakage is avoided.

The sudden change from heat to cold is just as dangerous. Glassware should never be removed from a closed cabinet where it has become heated, and brought immediately into contact with a cold substance. Cool the glass for a time in water before subjecting it to the extreme temperature.

RICH CUT GLASS

We sell only the finest quality of Rich Cut Glass, and guarantee every piece as represented

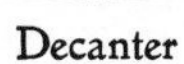

Decanter

Finger Bowl

Goblet

Tumbler

Claret Jug

4606. STEM WARE. "NAPOLEON"

This cutting can also be had on the bell shape, as shown on opposite page

	Per doz.	Bell shape
Goblets	$21 50	$23 00
Saucer Champ .	21 50	23 00
Clarets	19 80	21 35
Wines	15 25	17 00
Sherries . . . ,	16 50	18 00

	Per doz.	Bell shape
Cordials . . .	$14 50	$17 00
Champ. Tumblers	15 00	16 50
Finger Bowls .	21 45	24 00
Finger Bowl Plates	33 00	36 00
Water Tumblers .	16 50	18 00
Handled Lemonades	18 00	20 00

			Bell shape
Whiskey Tumblers,	doz.	$14 85	$16 00
Pt. Decanter, Squat,	each,	8 25	8 25
Qt. Decanter, Squat	"	10 00	10 00
Pint Claret Jug	"	10 00	10 00
Quart Claret Jug	"	11 50	11 50

RICH CUT GLASS—Continued

Decanter

Finger Bowl

Goblet

Tumbler

Handled Decanter

4607. STEM WARE. FLORENCE

Goblets	per doz.,	$34 50
Saucer Champ.	"	33 75
Clarets	"	27 25
Wines	"	24 75
Sherries	"	25 50
Tall Champ.	"	34 50
Cordials	per doz.,	$24 00
Champ. Tumblers	"	27 00
Finger Bowls	"	36 00
Finger Bowl Plates	"	46 50
Water Tumblers	"	31 50
Whiskey Tumblers	"	25 50
Pint Decanter, Squat	each,	$
Quart Decanter, Squat	"	22 50
Pint Claret Jug	"	
Quart Claret Jug	"	27 50
Handled Lemonades	per doz.,	30 00

RICH CUT GLASS—Continued

Decanter

Finger Bowl

Goblet

Tumbler

Claret Jug

4608. STEM WARE. THE H. & S.

Goblets	per doz.,	$19 35
Saucer Champ.	"	18 70
Clarets	"	16 00
Wines	"	14 70
Handled Lemonades	"	13 35
Sherries	per doz.,	$14 70
Cordials	"	13 35
Champ. Tumblers	"	14 70
Water Tumblers	"	16 00
Whiskey Tumblers	"	13 35
Finger Bowls	per doz.,	$17 35
Quart Decanter	each,	8 70
Quart Claret Jug	"	10 00
Pint Decanter	"	7 35
Pint Claret Jug	"	8 70

RICH CUT GLASS—Continued

Decanter

Finger Bowl

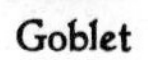
Goblet

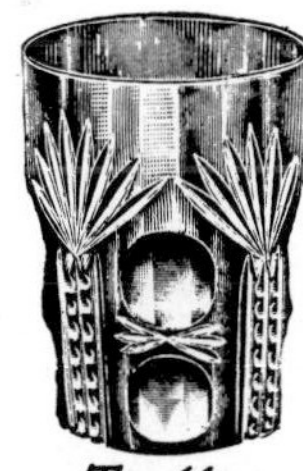
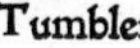
Tumbler

Claret Jug

4709. STEM WARE. "SPECIAL FLORENTINE"

Goblets	per doz.,	$18 00
Saucer Champ.	"	18 00
Clarets	"	14 25
Wines	"	12 75
Sherries	"	12 75
Cordials	per doz.,	$12 75
Champ. Tumblers	"	11 25
Finger Bowls	"	15 75
Water Tumblers	"	12 00
Handled Lemonades	"	14 25
Whiskey Tumblers	per doz.,	$9 75
Pint Decanter, Squat	each,	7 25
Quart Decanter, Squat	"	8 75
Pint Claret Jug	"	8 75
Quart Claret Jug	"	10 25

RICH CUT GLASS—Continued

Decanter

Finger Bowl

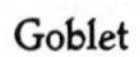

Goblet

Tumbler

Claret Jug

4610. STEM WEAR
STRAWBERRY DIAMOND AND FAN CUTTING

Goblets	per doz.,	$15 75
Saucer Champ.	"	15 75
Clarets	"	13 60
Wines	"	12 35
Sherries	"	13 25
Cordials	"	12 00
Lemonades, Handled	"	13 35

Water Tumblers	per doz.,	$12 00
Champ. Tumblers	"	11 50
Champ. Tall.	"	15 75
Finger Bowls	"	15 85
Finger Bowl Plates	"	28 00
Whiskey Tumblers	"	10 65

½-Pint Decanter, Squat	each,	$5 30
Pint Decanter, Squat	"	6 70
Quart Decanter, Squat	"	8 00
½-Pint Claret Jug	"	6 90
Pint Claret Jug	"	8 00
Quart Claret Jug	"	9 35
Quart Water Bottle	"	2 75

RICH CUT GLASS—Continued

Decanter

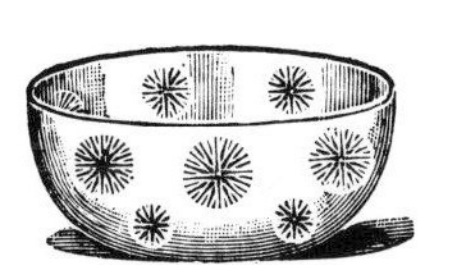

Finger Bowl

Goblet

Tumbler

Claret Jug

No. 4611

9432. SHAPE, CANADA, CUT STAR DESIGN, ALSO CUT STEMS AND CUT STAR BOTTOM

Goblets	per doz.,	$9 45	Water Tumblers	per doz.,	$5 05	Quart Decanter	each,	$2 25
Saucer Champ	"	9 45	Champ. Tumblers	"	4 55	Pint Decanter	"	2 00
Clarets	"	7 65	Whiskey Tumblers	"	4 35	Quart Claret Jug	"	3 15
Wines	"	6 55	Handled Lemonades	"	8 05	Pint Claret Jug	"	2 80
Sherries	"	6 55	Finger Bowls	"	9 85	Water Bottle	"	1 80
Cordials	"	5 45	Finger Bowl Plates	"	10 85	Oils	"	1 35

RICH CUT GLASS—Continued

Decanter

Finger Bowl

Goblet

Water Tumbler

Handled Decanter

4612. WEBB'S ROCK CRYSTAL GLASS WARE

Goblets	per doz.,	$36	50
Saucer Champ.	"	28	50
Clarets	"	23	00
Wines	"	19	00
Cordials	per doz.,	$17	50
Water Tumblers	"	27	50
Whiskey Tumblers	"	22	50
Finger Bowls	"	47	00
Finger Bowl Plates	per doz.,	$47	00
Quart Decanter	each,	14	00
Quart Claret Jug	"	18	75

RICH CUT GLASS—Continued

No. 4613

Handled Decanter
"Electric"

15 inches high . each, $18 00

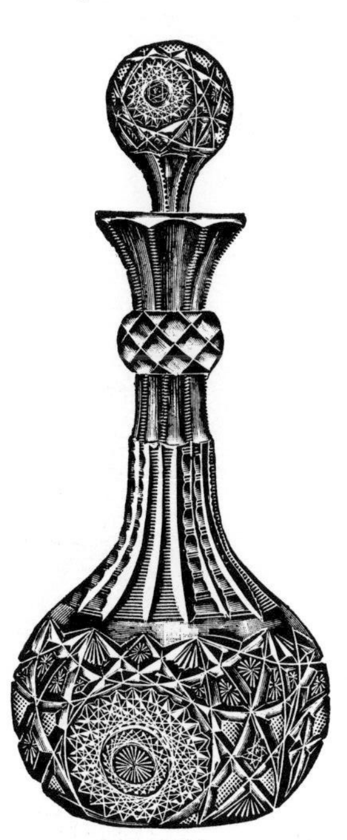

No. 4614

Decanter
"Electric"

15 inches high . each, $18 00

No. 4615

Handled Decanter
"Georgia"

13 in. high . . each, $12 00

No. 4616

Whiskey Decanter
"Georgia"

13 inches high . each, $10 00

RICH CUT GLASS—Continued

No. 4617

Whiskey Set. "Webster"

One Whiskey Jug, Six Glasses, one Mirror Tray . . . . .Set complete, $27 00

No. 4618

Whiskey Set. "Concord"

One Whiskey Jug, six Whiskey Glasses, one handled Mirror Tray . . . . . Set complete, $17 00

RICH CUT GLASS—Continued

No. 4619

Whiskey Set. "Syrott"

One Whiskey Jug, six Whiskey Glasses, one handled Mirror Tray . . . . Set complete, $17 00

No. 4620

Whiskey Set. "Manilla"

One Whiskey Decanter, six Whiskey Glasses, one Handled Mirror Tray . . . . Set complete, **$16 75**

RICH CUT GLASS—Continued

No. 4621

Whiskey Set. "Colonial"

One Decanter, six Whiskey Glasses, one handled Mirror Tray . . . . Complete, $8 00

No. 4622

Cordial Set. "Henrietta"

One Cordial Decanter, six Cordial Glasses, one Mirror Tray . . . . Set complete, $16 00

Complete line of the "Colonial" cutting is carried in stock; prices on application

RICH CUT GLASS—Continued

No. 4623

Cut Glass Set. "Dewey"

Twelve Saucer Champagnes, Twelve Water Tumblers, Twelve Wines, Twelve Sherries, Twelve Cordials, Sixty pieces . . . . Set complete, $48 50

Price list of separate pieces below :

Goblets	doz.,	$13 50	Lemonades . . .	doz.,	$9 00
Saucer Champ. .	"	13 50	Finger Bowls. . .	"	14 40
Clarets	"	10 75	Finger " plates	"	15 25
Wines	"	9 00	Hdl. Lemonade "	"	10 80
Sherries.	"	9 00	Pint Decanter. . .	ea.,	3 45
Cordials	"	7 50	Quart " . . .	"	4 00
Water Tumblers	"	10 00	" Hdl. " . . .	"	4 95
Whiskey "	"	6 50	Pint " " . . .	"	4 35
Champ. "	"	7 95			

No. 4624

Cut Glass Punch Bowl

"Webster"

14 inches. $45 00

RICH CUT GLASS—Continued

No. 4625

Punch Bowl. "Comet"

On foot. Beautiful combination of Chrysanthemum and bull's-eye cutting. Very heavy glass. Deeply and beautifully cut. Handsomely polished. 12½ inches across at top. Height, 15 inches. $60 00

No. 4626

Cut Glass Punch Bowl, on Foot. "Leader"

14 inches high ; 14 inches across $40 00

RICH CUT GLASS—Continued

No. 4627

No. 8628.—Punch Bowl

"Napoleon"

14 inches . . . . each, $33 00

Silver Plated Punch Ladle, Cut Glass Handle.

Plated . . . . each, $9 35

Solid Silver . . . . " 20 00

No. 4628

No. 4629

Cut Glass Punch Bowl

"Bedford"

Very rich and deeply cut. Handsomely polished

14 inches across . . . . each, $25 00

RICH CUT GLASS—Continued

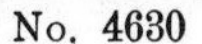

No. 4630

Nappie or Low Fruit, Salad or Berry Bowl. "Tornado"

8 inches	each,	$8 25
9 inches	"	10 50
10 inches	"	13 50

No. 4631

Salad Bowl. "Tornado"

8 inches	each,	$10 50
9 inches	"	13 50
10 inches	"	18 00

No. 4632

Salad, Fruit or Berry Bowl "Sloan"

8 inches	each,	$6 25
9 inches	"	8 25
10 inches	"	10 50

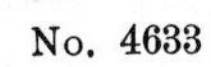

No. 4633

Salad, Fruit or Berry Bowl with Tray "Peerless"

Bowl, 10 inches across
Tray, 12 " "

2 pieces $35 00

No. 4634

Nappie or Low Salad or Berry Bowl "Sloan"

8 inches	each,	$5 75
9 inches	"	7 50
10 inches	"	9 75

RICH CUT GLASS—Continued.

No. 4635

Rich Cut Glass Bowl. "Jubilee"

8 inches	each,	$14 25
9 "	"	18 00
10 "	"	22 50

No. 4636

Cut Glass Bowl. "Monarch"

8 inches	each,	$15 00
9 "	"	18 00
10 "	"	22 00

No. 4637

Fruit, Salad or Berry Bowl. "Webster"

8 inches	each,	$9 75
9 "	"	12 00
10 "	"	15 00

No. 4638

Cut Glass Fruit, Salad or Berry Bowl "Webster"

8 inches	each,	$9 75
9 "	"	12 00
10 "	"	15 00

No. 4639

Nut, Fruit or Berry Bowl. "Webster"

8 inches	each,	$7 90
9 "	"	9 75
10 "	"	12 00

No. 4640

Cut Glass Nappie or Berry Bowl. "Glen"

8 inches	each,	$12 00
9 "	"	15 00
10 "	"	18 00

RICH CUT GLASS—Continued

No. 4641

Cut Glass Nappie. "Monarch"

8 inches	each,	$12 00
9 "	"	15 00
10 "	"	18 00

No. 4642

Cut Glass Nappie. "Arlington"

8 inches	each,	$4 50
9 "	"	5 75
10 "	"	7 25

No. 4643

Cut Glass Nappie. "Castleton"

7 inches	each,	$3 00
8 "	"	3 50
9 "	"	4 25
10 "	"	5 25

No. 4644

Cut Glass Bowl. "Arlington"

8 inches	each,	$5 75
9 "	"	7 50
10 "	"	9 35

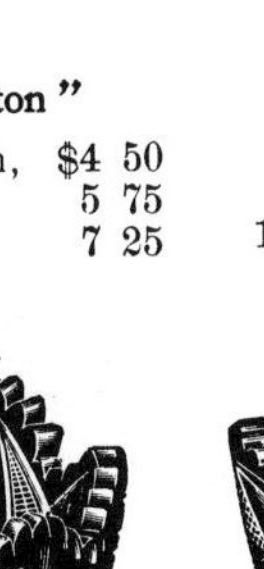

No. 4645

Cut Glass Salad Bowl. "Lisbon"

8 inches . . . . each, $3 75

No. 4646

Salad Bowl. "Coronet"

8 inches . . . . each, $5 00

RICH CUT GLASS

(Continued)

No. 4647

Celery Dish. "Webster"

11½ inches long . . . each, $8 60

No. 4649

Cut Glass Celery Tray. "Arlington"

11½ x 4¼ inches . . . each, $5 75

No. 4648

Celery Dish—No. 662

5½ x 12 inches . each, $9 00

No. 4652.

Cut Glass Celery Tray "Delhi"

4½ x 11¾ inches . . . each, $3 75

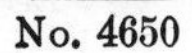

No. 4650

Celery Tray. "St. Cloud"

4 x 11½ inches . . . . each, $6 00

No. 4651

Cut Glass Celery. "Aetna"

Two Chrysanthemums in bottom, scallop cut edge

4½ x 12 inches $5 00

RICH CUT GLASS

(Continued)

No. 4653

Ice Tub. "Webster"

5 inches across; 4½ inches to top of handles, each, $10 50

No. 4654

Covered Cheese. "Webster"

Plate, 9 inches across . . . . . . Complete, $18 00

No. 4655

Cut Glass Handled Ice Tub "Arlington"

7 inches across handles; height, 4¼ inches, with drainer $10 50

No. 4656

Ice Tub. "The Estelle"

4¾ inches opening; height, 4 inches . . . . . each, $6 75

No. 4657

Cut Glass Ice Tub. "Admiral"

4 inches to top of handles; 6 inches across . . . each, $6 75

RICH CUT GLASS

Continued

No. 4658

Ice Tub and Plate. "Napoleon"

Each $18 00

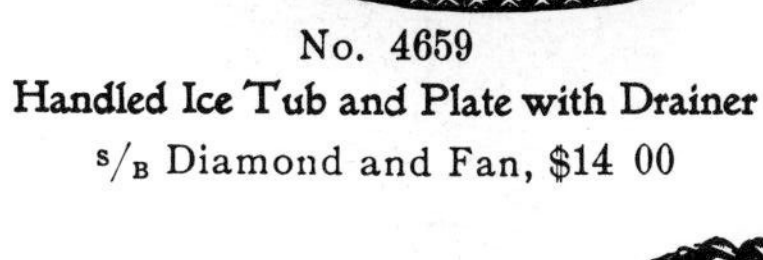

No. 4659

Handled Ice Tub and Plate with Drainer

S/B Diamond and Fan, $14 00

No. 4660

Ice Bowl. "Belvedere"

On foot. 5 inches high. 9 inches from handle to handle. Each, $7 00

No. 4661

Butter Tub and Plate. "Napoleon"

Each $11 55

No. 4662

Fruit or Berry Bowl. "Florida"

9¼ x 13½ . . . . each, $10 35

RICH CUT GLASS—Continued

No. 4663—**Water Bottle. "Napoleon"**
One quart . . . . each, $5 75

No. 4664—**Water Bottle. "Webster"**
One quart . . . . each, $6 75

No. 4665—**Water Bottle. "Kenmore"**
One quart . . . . each, $3 00

No. 4666—**Water Bottle. "Tornado"**
Each $7 85

No. 4667—**Water Bottle**
S/B Diamond Fan, one quart, each, $1 80

No. 4668—**Water Bottle. "Monarch"**
One quart . . . . each, $14 00

RICH CUT GLASS—Continued

No. 4669

Cut Glass Jug. "Otis"

2 Quarts . . . . cach, $10 00
1 Quart . . . . " 7 50

No. 4670

Claret Jug. "Lakeland"

3 Pints, 11 inches high . . each, $11 25

No. 4671

Cut Glass Jug. "Dewey"

2 Quarts . . . . cach, $12 00
1 Quart . . . . " 9 00

RICH CUT GLASS—Continued

No. 4672

Tankard Jug

S/B Diamond and Fan

½ Pint	each,	$4 70
1 Pint	"	5 35
1 Quart	"	6 70
3 Pints	"	8 70
2 Quarts	"	11 35

No. 4673

Tankard Jug

S/B Diamond and Fan

No. 003-4, 1 Quart	each,	$1 75
" 003-5, 2½ Pints	"	2 00
" 003-6, 3 Pints	"	2 25
" 003-7, 2 Quarts	"	2 65

No. 4674

Wide Mouth Jug

S/B Diamond and Fan

⅓ Pint	each,	$4 00
½ Pint	"	5 35
1 Pint	"	7 00
1 Quart	"	9 35
3 Pints	"	10 67

RICH CUT GLASS—Continued

No. 4675

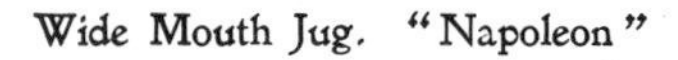

Wide Mouth Jug. "Napoleon"

1 Pint . . . . each,	$8 65
1 Quart . . . . "	11 50
3 Pints . . . . "	13 20

No. 4676

Cut Glass Vase. "India"

12 inches high . . . . each, $15 00

No. 4677

Claret Jug. "Amazon"

Richly Cut Glass with Sterling Silver hand-chased mounting.

2 Pints	$8 50
3 Pints	12 75

CUT GLASS. STERLING SILVER MOUNTINGS

Rich Cut Glass Jugs, with extra heavy Sterling Silver hand-chased tops

No. 4678

Cut Glass Claret Pitcher. "Syrott"

Prism and Bead Cutting, heavily mounted with Sterling Silver top, richly chased.

1 Quart . . . . each, $12 00
3 Pints . . . . " 16 50

No. 4679

Cut Glass Claret Pitcher. "Maine"

With heavy Sterling Silver top

1 Quart . . . . each, $10 15
3 Pints . . . . " 13 50

No. 4680

Cut Glass Claret Pitcher. "Lakeland"

Sterling Silver mounted

1 Quart . . . . each, $12 00
3 Pints . . . . " 18 00

RICH CUT GLASS—Continued

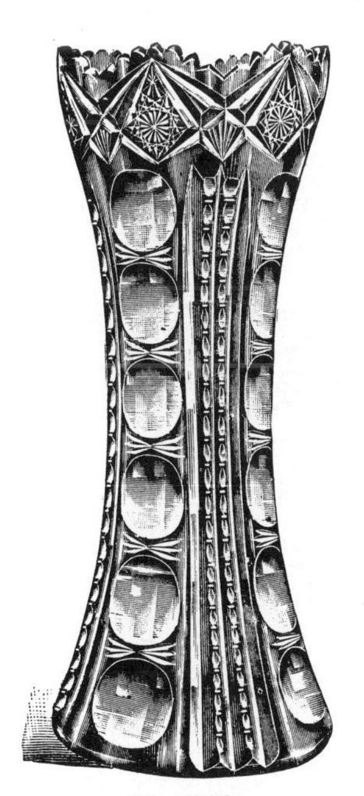

No. 4681

No. 8101—Cut Glass Vase "Florentine"

8	inches high,	each,	$5 25
10	"	"	"	6 75
12	"	"	"	8 25

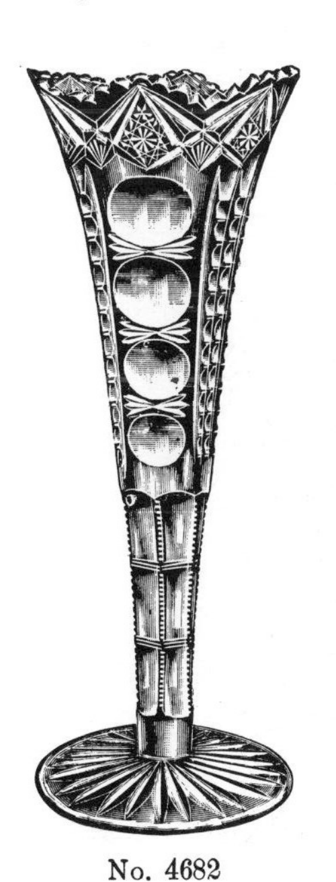

No. 4682

Flower Vase. "Florentine"

8	inches high,	each,	$2 35
10	"	"	"	3 00
12	"	"	"	4 00
14	"	"	"	5 35
16	"	"	"	6 70

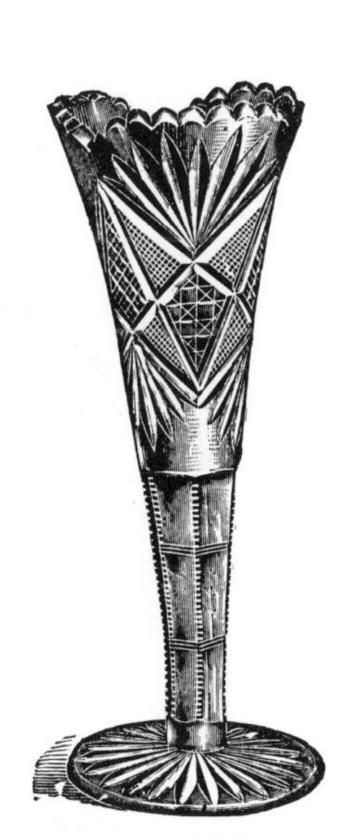

No. 4683

Flower Vase. "Everett"

8	inches high,	each,	$1 90
10	"	"	"	3 00
12	"	"	"	4 00
14	"	"	"	5 00
16	"	"	"	6 50

No. 4684

Flower Vase. "B 9/602"

9	inches high,	each,	$6 75
10	"	"	"	8 25
12	"	"	"	10·50

RICH CUT GLASS

Continued

No. 4685

Cut Glass Lamp

"Chrysanthemum"

Height to top of chimney, 23 inches
Complete $50 00

No. 4686

Cut Glass Rose Bowl
"Caprice"

6 inches	$9 75
7 "	12 00
8 "	13 75
9 "	18 00

No. 4687
Rich Cut Glass Lamp
Height to top of chimney, 21 inches
Complete $25 00

RICH CUT GLASS—Continued

No. 4688

Mayonnaise Bowl with Plate
"Napoleon"

6 inches across . . . 2 pieces, $9 00

No. 4689

Covered Cheese. "New York"
l/s Plate, 10 inches across, and cut same as cover. . . . . complete, $13 50
s/s Plate, 9 in. and cut same as cover, comp., 12 00

No. 4690

Mayonnaise Dish with Tray
"Imperial" No. 004

6 inches across. . . .2 pieces, $7 50

No. 4691

Mayonnaise Bowl with Plate
"Florentine"

6 inches across . . . 2 pieces, $7 25

No. 4692

Handled Bon Bon. "Arlington"

6 inches . . . . each, $2 25

No. 4693

No. 9157—Cigar Cutter and Ash Receiver

Rich cut glass and sterling silver
4 inches across

Each, ...$5 35

RICH CUT GLASS—Continued

No. 4694

Ice Cream Tray. "Arlington"

8½ x 13½ inches $12 75

No. 4695

Ice Cream Saucer or Bon-Bon. "Arlington"

6 inches. . . . . .per doz. $24 00
5 " . . . . " 21 00

No. 4696

Ice Cream Saucer. "Webster"

6 inches. . . . . .per doz. $42 00
5 " . . . . " 33 00

No. 4697

Ice Cream Tray. "Webster"

14 x 8½ inches . . . . each, $18 00

RICH CUT GLASS—Continued

No. 4698

Spoon Holder. "Webster"

4½ inches high . . . . each, $5 00

No. 4699

Ice Cream Saucer. "Washington"

6 inches . . . . . per doz., $27 00

No. 4700

Spoon Holder, Double Handled "Wheeler"

4½ inches . . . . each, $4 15

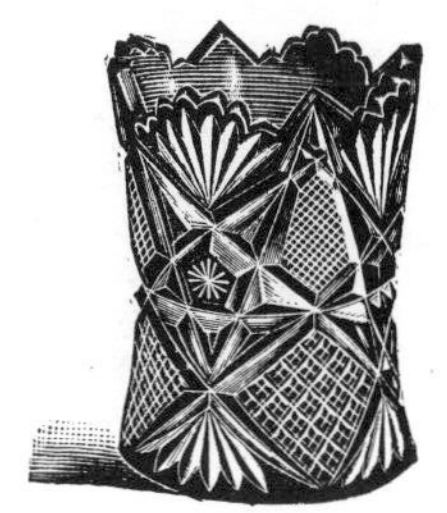

No. 4701

Spooner, Cut. "Florence"

4½ inches high. 3-inch opening.

Each $3 75

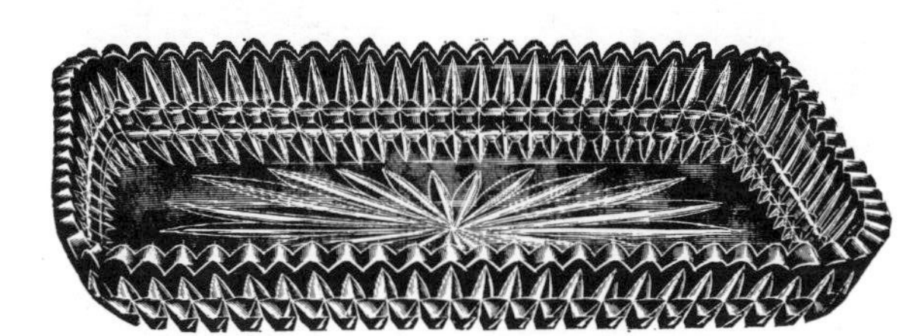

No. 4702

Ice Cream Tray. "Renaissance"

8 x 12 . . . . each, $6 75

No. 4703

Spooner. "Napoleon"

Each $5 75

RICH CUT GLASS—Continued

No. 4704

Cigar Jar "Renaissance"

Top made hollow for holding sponge.

For Holding

50 Cigars, White . .	$7 25
25 " " . .	4 95
50 " Green . .	11 10
25 " " . .	7 00

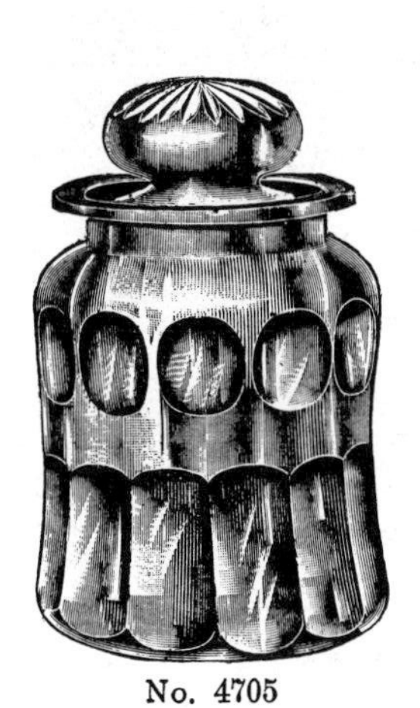

No. 4705

Cigar Jar

Top made hollow for holding sponge.

For Holding

50 Cigars, White . .	$7 25
25 " " . .	4 95
50 " Green . .	11 00
25 " " . .	7 00

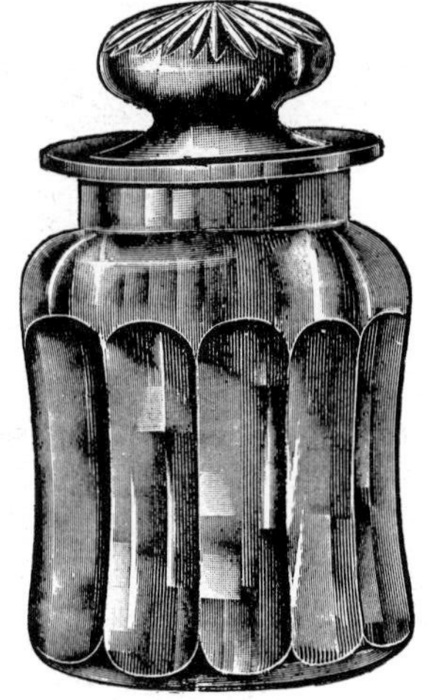

No. 4706

Cigar Jar

Top is made hollow for inserting sponge.

For Holding

50 Cigars, White . .	$6 30
25 " " . .	4 35
50 " Green . .	10 00
25 " " . .	6 60

No. 4707

Cigar Jar. "Majestic"

Height, 6½ inches.

Cover made for inserting sponge

Each $6 00

TANTALUS SETS AND CIGAR JARS

No. 4708

Cigar Jar

With frame in either mahogany or antique oak $20 00
Holds 50 cigars
Richer cuttings described and priced on request

No. 4709

Wine Set. "Georgia"

With 3 bottles	$40 00
With 2 bottles	30 00
Same set arranged with 3 bottles and 12 tumblers to match..	59 00
Same set arranged with 2 bottles and 6 tumblers to match..	40 50

Frames either in mahogany or antique oak

No. 4710

Whiskey Set. "Dewey"

2 bottles with frame . . . $21.00
Above fitted with whiskey jug "Manilla," illustrated on first page following, complete . . . $28 00
Frame either mahogany or antique oak

RICH CUT GLASS

Continued

No. 4711

Whiskey Decanter. "Renaissance"

Yacht shape

White .... each, $5 00
Green or Ruby .... " 6 30

No. 4712

Whiskey Jug. "Manilla"

Each.................................... $9 00

No. 4713

Whiskey Decanter. Yacht Shape

Cut Stopper, Star Cut Bottom

White............................... each, $3 75
Green.................................. " 4 95
Ruby .... " 4 95

No. 4714

No. 4715

Vinegar or Oil Bottle

No. 4716

Vinegar or Oil Bottle

No. 4717

RICH CUT GLASS—Continued

No. 4718
Horse Radish Jar
"Napoleon"
5¼ inches high . . . $4 25

No. 4719
Horse Radish Jar
"H. & S"
5¼ inches high . . . $3 75

No. 4720
Horse Radish Jar
S/B Diamond and Fan
5¼ inches high, each, $3 75

No. 4721
Horse Radish Jar
"Renaissance"
5¼ inches high . . . $2 75

No. 4722
Salt or Pepper Shaker
Sterling tops. Either for salt or pepper
Cut prism and bead
Each $0 75

No. 4723
Pepper Shaker
Cut prism and bead. Sterling top
Each $0 75

No. 4724
Salt or Pepper Shaker
Sterling tops. Either for salt or pepper
Cut prism and bead
Each $0 75

RICH CUT GLASS—Continued

No. 4725

No. 6232—**Catsup Bottle, large neck**

Height, 7 inches. Shape 22. Cut Strawberry Diamond and Fan

Each $3 00

No. 4726

½ Pint Tumbler

Strawberry Diamond and Fan.

Per dozen $8 75

Same tumblers as above, only not cut quite as deep

Per dozen . . . . . $5 00 and $2 50

No. 4727

No. 07154—**Catsup Bottle, large neck**

Height, 7 inches. Shape 22. Heavy cut stopper

Each $4 00

No. 4728

Worcestershire Bottle

Height, 8 inches. Strawberry Diamond and Fan Cutting

Each $2 25

No. 4729

Tabasco Sauce Bottle

Silver-plated stopper. Strawberry Diamond and Fan Cutting

Each $2 10

No. 4730

Cuba. ½ Pint Handled Oil

Rich Deep Cutting

Each $1 50

No. 4731

Worcestershire Bottle "Majestic"

Rich Deep Cutting

Each $4 50

RICH CUT GLASS—Continued

No. 4732

½-Pint Oil or Vinegar Bottle "Napoleon"

Each $3 30

No. 4733

Oil or Vinegar Bottle "Webster"

Each $5 25

No. 4734

Oil or Vinegar Cruet

Small size, 5 inches high, prism cutting, star cut bottom and cut handle

Each $2 65

No. 4735

½-Pint Handled Oil

Strawberry Diamond and Fan.

Each $1 25

No. 4736

Mustard or Horse Radish Jar

Each $1 75

No. 4737

Mustard or Horse Radish Jar "Renaissance"

Each $2 25

No. 4738

Mustard or Horse Radish Jar "Napoleon"

Each $2 75

RICH CUT GLASS—Continued

No. 4739

Sugar and Creamer. "Webster"

Sugar, 3-inch opening. Creamer, 2½ inch opening

Per set $9 00

No. 4740

Sugar and Creamer. "Arlington"

Two Pieces $5 25

No. 4741

Sugar and Creamer. "Washington"

Heavy, rich cut, and chrysanthemum star bottom. Sugar, 3-inch opening. Creamer, 3-inch opening

Price . . . . per set, $5 00

No. 4742

Sugar and Creamer. "Be vedere"

Sugar, 5¼ inches from outside of handles. Creamer, 4¼ inches from lip to outside of handle

Price . . . . per set, $4 50

RICH CUT GLASS—Continued

No. 4743

Sugar and Creamer. "Arlington"

Sugar Handled, 2 pieces $6 00

No. 4744

Ice Cream Saucer, Olive or Bon Bon. "Napoleon"

6 inches . . . . each, $2 25

$27 00 per dozen

No. 4745

Low Spoon Holder or Salted Almond

Rich Chrysanthemum cutting

7¼ inches long

Each $3 00

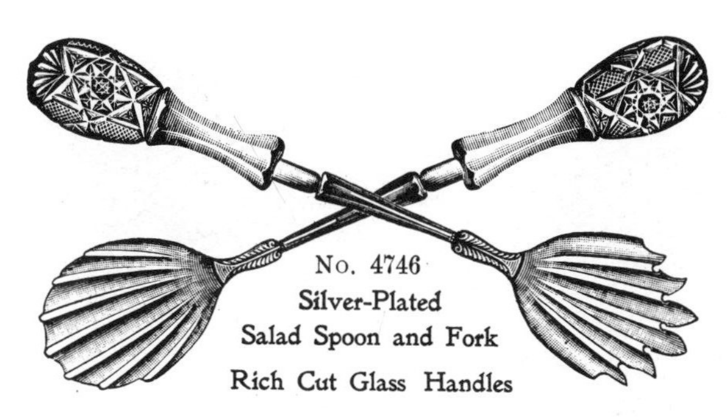

No. 4746

Silver-Plated Salad Spoon and Fork

Rich Cut Glass Handles

$10 70 pair

Solid Silver, Gold Lined . . . . pair, $22 50

No. 4747

Cologne Bottle. "St. Julien"

4 ounce . . . . $3 00 8 ounce $4 50
6 " . . . . 3 75 12 " 5 75

RICH CUT GLASS—Continued

No. 4748

No. 051-9—Oval Olive, Pickle or Bon Bon
"Walter Scott"

4 x 7 inches . . . . each, $3 10

No. 4749

No. 051-4—Olive or Bon Bon
"Walter Scott"

3½ x 6¾ inches . . . . . . each, $3 10

No. 4750

No. 051-11—Oblong Olive, Pickle or Bon Bon. "Walter Scott"

4 x 7 inches . . . . each, $3 10

No. 4751

No. 065—Olive or Bon Bon
"Walter Scott"

5½ inches . . . . each, $3 10

No. 4752

Olive or Bon Bon, Heart Shape
"Walter Scott"

5½ x 5 inches . . . . each, $3 10

No. 4753

No. 051-6—Olive or Bon Bon
"Walter Scott"

6 inches . . . . each, $3 10

RICH CUT GLASS—Continued

No. 4754

No. 5701—Olive or Bon Bon
"Walter Scott"
Square Shape
5¾ inches across . . . . . . each, $3 10

No. 4755

No. 051-5—Oblong Olive, Pickle or Bon Bon. "Walter Scott"
4 x 8 inches . . . . each, $3 10

No. 4756

No. 051-3—Olive or Bon Bon
"Walter Scott"
3¼ x 6⅝ inches . . . . . . each, $3 10

No. 4757

No. 051-2—Spoon Holder or Olive
"Walter Scott"
4 x 7 inches . . . . each, $3 10

No. 4758

Violet Holder. "Napoleon"
4½ inches high . . . . each, $2 00

No. 4759

Cut Glass Dish. "Elite"
Particularly adapted for butter balls, radishes, etc., sides being perfectly straight
5½ inches across . . . . . . each, $2 65

RICH CUT GLASS—Continued

No. 4760

Handled Nappy or Bon Bon
"Gem"

5 inches . . . . each, $1 50

No. 4761

Handled Nappy or Bon Bon
"Alaska"

5½ inches. . . . . each, $2 00

No. 4762

Handled Nappy or Bon Bon. "Clover"
Leaf Shape

Each $3 00

No. 4763

Salted Almond Dish
"Webster"

3¼ x 6 inches . . . . each, $3 75

No. 4764

Handled Nappy or Bon Bon
"Webster"

6 inches . . . . each, $3 85

No. 4765

Handled Nappy or Bon Bon
"Jubilee"

6 inches . . . . each, $5 75

BOHEMIAN GLASS NOVELTIES

No. 4766

Syrup Jug

Plated top and handle
4 inches high
Each $0 85

No. 4767

No. 8727—**Toothpick Holder**

Each $0 30

No. 4768

No. 88—**Syrup Jug**

Height, 6 inches
Each $1 35

No. 4769

No. 4737—**Mustard Pot**

Height, 3 inches
Each $0 85

No. 4770

Salt Shaker

s/B Diamond and Fan
Each. $0 15

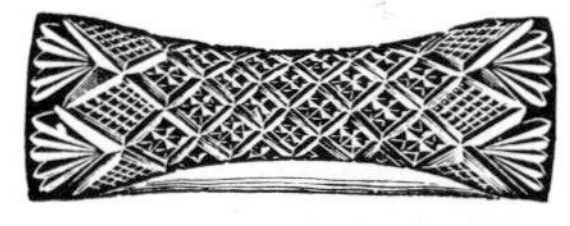

No. 4771

No. 981—**Knife Rest**

4 inches long . . each, $0 50

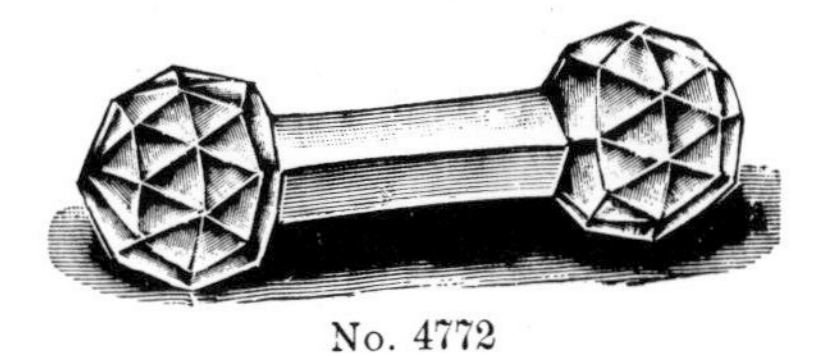

No. 4772

Knife Rest

Lapidary Cutting

4	inches long,	each,	$0 50
4¼	"	"	"	0 75
5	"	"	"	1 00

No. 4773

Indv. Olive or Salted Almond

Size, 3 x 5 inches
Each $0 50

No. 4774

Pepper Shaker

s/B Diamond and Fan
Each $0 15

Goblet showing Monogram and Wreath in Raised Gold

Goblet showing Three-Letter Monogram Cut and Gilded

Special Ornamentation of Glass and China

Nothing is more gratifying to persons of taste and refinement than the possession of articles which are *individualized*—differing from those of other people, if not in design and material, then through marking or decoration. As is well known, those who can afford it often go to great expense in such matters, while others are glad to pay proportionately smaller sums to gratify the same natural inclination.

To all such persons the special decoration of Glass and China appeals with great force, and the demand, therefor, we find to be growing from year to year. Fortunately our facilities keep pace with this demand, and there is probably no house in the country better qualified for service of this description than ours. So well is this understood, that when something special is wanted at short notice, application is made here at once. For instance, at the reception given to Admiral Dewey and wife by the Union League Club of Brooklyn, Higgins & Seiter not only furnished the china for the dinner, but the name of each guest was burned upon the plate set at his place, and the plate used instead of a card to designate where he should sit. The plates were afterwards sent home to the guests as souvenirs.

Special Ornamentation

We are constantly filling orders for Special Marking and Ornamentation from Clubs and yacht owners, as well as for individuals, and private use, and especially for wedding and anniversary gifts. The opportunity here is very great, inasmuch as the favorite color, symbol, device or motto can be selected, and thus something can be produced that is not only unique, with no probability of duplication, but in exact accordance with the individual taste or hobby of the recipient. It goes without saying how much more such a gift is likely to be prized than the more expensive article which can be bought anywhere at a moment's notice.

We take pleasure in submitting original designs for initials, monograms, etc, or in working out suggestions submitted for the purpose ; and will reproduce crests, coats of arms, etc., with fidelity and taste. We cheerfully answer any inquiries, and quote prices for the ornamentation of single pieces or whole sets—for original designs, or for matching those already in existence, guaranteeing always satisfactory work and prompt and safe delivery.

Plate showing yacht signal decorated in color

Goblet showing yacht signal decorated in color

GOLD GLASS

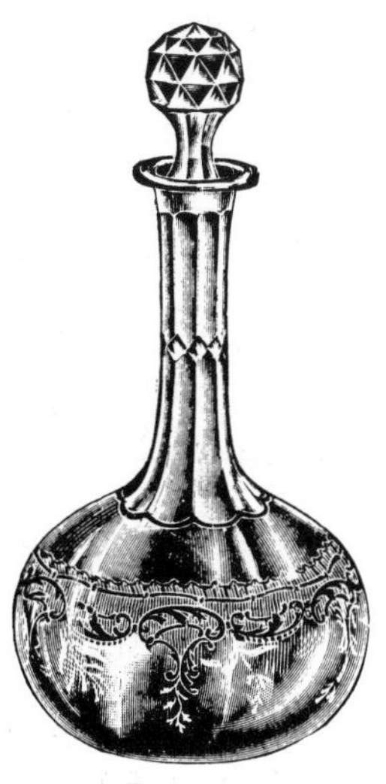
Decanter

Finger Bowl

Goblet

Tumbler

Claret Jug

No. 4775

No. 7931—Etched border design with rococo gold. Gold edge and gold line on foot : cut stem

Goblets	per doz.,	$12 25	Water Tumblers No, 3	per doz.,	$10 45	Decanter, quart	each,	$3 45
Claret, R. B	"	9 75	Whiskey Tumblers taper	"	6 85	Decanter, pint	"	3 15
Cocktail	"	8 30	Champ. Tumblers	"	7 95	Decanter, ½ pint	"	2 55
Champ. Saucer	"	12 25	Finger Bowls	"	14 40	Decanter, handled, quart	"	4 80
Wines	"	8 30	Handled Lemonades	"	12 60	Decanter, handled, pint	"	4 35
Cordials	"	7 20	Oil Bottles	each,	1 85	Decanter, handled, ½ pint	"	3 30
Sherries, flanged	"	8 30	Water Bottles	"	3 15			

GOLD DECORATED GLASS

Decanter

Finger Bowl

Goblet

Tumbler

Claret Jug

No. 4776

BACCARAT GLASS "NEWPORT PATTERN" GOLD DECORATION

This is an etched design filled with best burnished gold, also gold line on edge and foot of stem ware, and on handles and tops of all decanters

Goblets	per doz.,	$13 10
Champ. Saucer	"	13 10
Champ. Tall.	"	13 10
Clarets, R. B	"	11 25
Cocktails	"	10 00
Wines	"	10 00
Sherries	"	10 75
Cordials	"	8 75
Pousse Cafés	"	8 75

Water Tumblers, large size	per doz.,	$11 50
Water Tumblers, medium size	"	10 25
Champ. Tumblers . . .	"	9 10
Whiskey Tumblers . . .	"	8 30
Ale Tumblers	"	13 00
Lemonades, handled . .	"	12 35
Finger Bowls.	"	21 75

Finger Bowl Plates . . .	per doz.,	$25 00
Decanters, unhandled, ½ pint,	each,	3 00
Decanters, unhandled, pint	"	3 30
Decanters, unhandled, quarts,	each,	4 30
Decanters, handled, ½ pint . .	"	4 00
Decanters, handled, pint . . .	"	4 65
Decanters, handled, quart . .	"	5 90
Water Bottles	"	3 85
Oil Cruets, handled	"	3 45

GOLD DECORATED GLASS—Continued

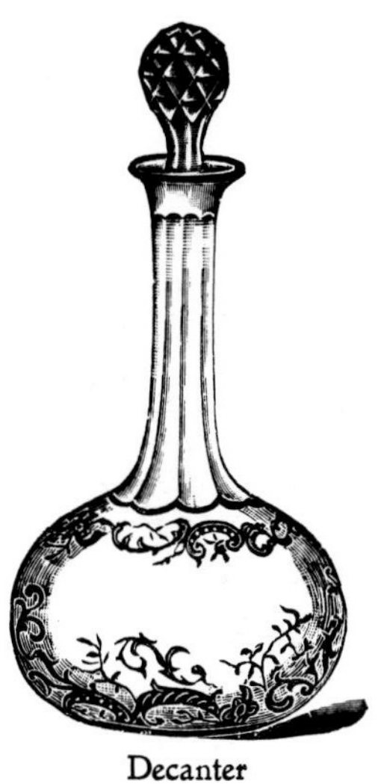

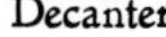
Decanter

Finger Bowl

Goblet

Tumbler

Claret Jug

No. 4777

No. 788—"SCHILLER." ETCHED GOLD

Rich etched gold rococo design, with cut stems and gold edge

Goblets	per doz.,	$15 95
Champ. Saucer	"	15 95
Clarets	"	14 10
Wines	"	12 70
Sherries	"	12 70
Cordials	"	10 50
Cocktails	"	11 75

Water Tumblers	per doz.,	$13 40
Champ. Tumblers	"	9 45
Whiskey Tumblers	"	9 45
Handled Lemonades	"	14 10
Finger Bowls	"	18 15
Finger Bowl Plates	"	16 35

Quart Decanter	each,	$4 55
Pint Decanter	"	3 90
Quart Claret Jug	"	5 30
Pint Claret Jug	"	5 00
Quart Water Bottle	"	3 80
Oils	"	2 30

This glass can be had plain. Prices on application

IRIDESCENT GLASS

Decanter

Finger Bowl

Goblet

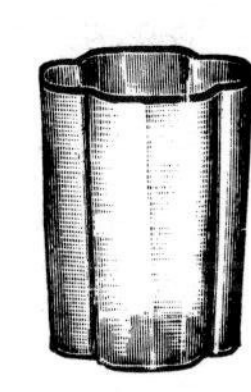

Tumbler

Claret Jug

No. 4778

IRIDESCENT GLASS. (S. 104)

Prismatic or rainbow coloring, with best burnished gold edge, decanter having gold line on handle, neck and stopper

Goblets	per doz.,	$7 50
Clarets	"	6 25
Wines	"	6 00
Cordials	"	4 25
Sherries	"	5 25
Champ. Saucer	"	7 50
Champ. Tumblers	"	4 50
Water Tumblers	"	5 25

Whiskey	per doz.,	$4 50
Finger Bowls	"	10 50
Finger Bowl Plates	"	13 25
Lemonades, handled	"	5 25
Pint Decanter	each,	1 95
½ Pint Decanter	"	1 70
Quart Decanter	"	2 25

Pint Claret Jug	each,	$2 25
½ Pint Claret Jug	"	1 95
Quart Claret Jug	"	2 80
Oil Bottle	"	1 40
Water Bottle	"	1 70
Spoon Holder	"	1 40
Celery Glass	"	1 70

ENGRAVED GLASSWARE

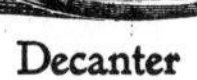

Decanter

Finger Bowl

Goblet

Tumbler

Claret Jug

No. 4779

BACCARAT GLASS. "NEWPORT"

No. 5086—Etched Border Design

Goblets	per doz.,	$4 80
Claret, R. B.	"	4 40
Cocktail	"	3 90
Champ. Saucer	"	5 25
Wines	"	3 90
Cordials	"	3 65
Sherries flanged	"	4 80
Water Tumblers, large	"	3 65
Water Tumblers, medium	per doz.,	$3 25
Whiskey Tumblers, taper	"	2 40
Appolinaris Tumblers	"	2 60
Champ. Tumblers	"	2 40
Preserve Saucers, 5 inch	"	7 30
Finger Bowls	"	9 30
Finger Bowl Plates	"	10 80
Handled Lemonades	"	5 25
Oil Bottles	each,	$1 90
Water Bottles	"	2 10
Decanter, quart	"	2 15
Decanter, pint	"	1 75
Decanter, ½ pint	"	1 65
Decanter, handled, quart	"	3 65
Decanter, handled, pint	"	2 85
Decanter, handled, ½ pint	"	2 40

ENGRAVED GLASSWARE—Continued

Decanter

Finger Bowl

Goblet

Tumbler

No. 4780

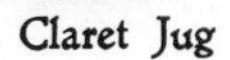

Claret Jug

No. 3241—BACCARAT GLASS, ETCHED

Goblets	per doz.,	$3 75
Clarets, R. B.	"	3 35
Clarets, plain	"	3 35
Saucer Champ.	"	3 75
Wines	"	3 00
Sherries	"	3 35
Cordials	"	2 75
Tumblers, large	"	2 75

Tumblers, medium . . .	per doz.,	$2 35
Champ. Tumblers	"	1 80
Whiskey Tumblers . . .	"	1 80
Finger Bowls	"	5 00
Finger Bowl Plates . . .	"	9 00
Lemonades, handled . . .	"	3 65
Pint Decanter, No. 10	each,	1 50
Quart Decanter, No. 11 . . .	"	1 70

Pint Claret Jug, No. 10 . . .	each,	$2 35
Quart Claret Jug, No. 11 . .	"	2 50
Cheese Dish, covered, large size	"	2 80
Cheese Dish, covered, small size	"	2 40
Spoon Holder	"	85
Celery Glass	"	1 35

ENGRAVED GLASSWARE—Continued

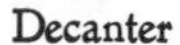
Decanter

Finger Bowl

Goblet

Tumbler

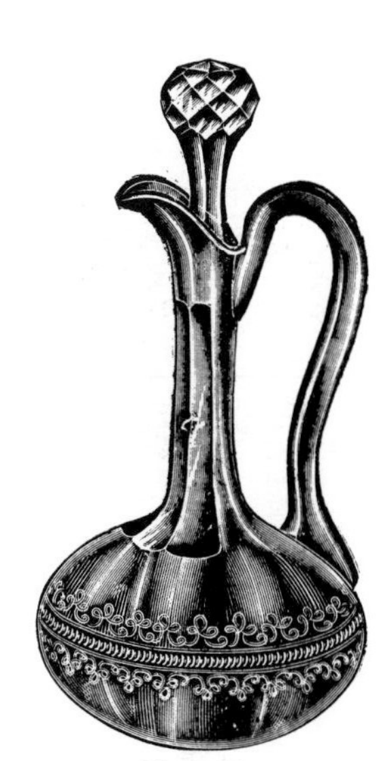
Claret Jug

No. 4781

No. 5531—ETCHED BORDER DESIGN

Goblets	per doz., $3 10	Water Tumblers	per doz., $2 00	Quart Decanter	each, $1 55
Saucer Champ.	" 3 10	Champ. Tumblers	" 1 50	Pint Decanter	" 1 30
Clarets	" 3 00	Whiskey Tumblers	" 1 60	Quart Claret Jug	" 2 45
Wines	" 2 45	Handled Lemonades	" 4 50	Pint Claret Jug	" 2 00
Sherries	" 3 00	Finger Bowls	" 4 70	Quart Water Bottle	" 1 25
Cordials	" 2 40	Finger Bowl Plates	" 8 30	Oils	" 1.10
Cocktails	" 3 00				

ENGRAVED GLASSWARE—Continued

Decanter

Finger Bowl

Goblet

Tumbler

Claret Jug

No. 4782

BOHEMIAN GLASS, ENGRAVED. No. 1

Goblets	per doz.	$2 85
Clarets, plain	"	2 35
Clarets, R. B.	"	2 35
Wines	"	1 70
Cordials	"	1 35
Sherries	"	2 50
Saucer Champ	"	3 00
Champ. Tumblers	"	1 25
Tumblers, large	per doz.	$1 55
Tumblers, medium	"	1 45
Whiskey	"	1 40
Finger Bowls	"	4 10
Lemonades, handled	"	2 00
Pint Decanter	each,	1 40
Quart Decanter	"	1 55
Pint Claret Jug	"	1 85
Quart Claret Jug	each,	$2 10
Oil Bottle	"	70
Water Bottle	"	1 40
Cheese Dish, covered, large size	"	1 75
Cheese Dish, small size	"	1 50
Spoon Holders	"	70
Celery Glass	"	1 40

GLASS SETS

No. 4783

Glass Set. No. 32

The glass is slightly fluted with flaring top with border of needle etching, as follows:

12 Saucer Champs., 12 Wines, 12 Clarets,
12 Cordials, 12 Water Tumblers,

60 pieces, complete $9 75

We also carry this line complete, prices of which we give herewith:

	Per doz.		Per doz.
Goblets	$2 60	Cordials	$2 20
Saucer Champ.	2 60	Pousse Cafés	2 20
R. B. Clarets	2 40	Water Tumblers, L. S.	1 30
Cocktails	2 30	Champ. Tumblers	1 20
Wines	2 30	Whiskey Tumblers	1 20
Sherries	2 30	Lemonades, handled	2 50

Finger Bowls . . per doz., $4 00

No. 4784

Glass Set. No. 442.

Etched fleur-de-lis design, with fancy etched border, as follows:

12 Saucer Champs, 12 Round Bowl Clarets,
12 Wines, 12 Cordials,
12 Water Tumblers.

60 pieces $7 60

We also carry this line complete, prices of which we give herewith:

	Per doz.		Per doz.
Goblets	$2 45	Brandy and Soda Tumblers	$1 10
Saucer Champs	2 45	Water Tumblers	80
Round Bowl Clarets	2 25	Small Beer Glass	80
Cocktails	2 20	Champ. Tumblers	80
Sherries	2 10	Whiskey Tumblers	80
Wines	2 00	Handled Lemonades	2 50
Cordials	1 95	Finger Bowls	2 80
Pousse Café	1 95		

GLASS SETS—Continued

No. 4785

Glass Sets

Plain Baccarat; as follows:
12 Saucer Champs., 12 Round Bowl Clarets,
12 Wines, 12 Cordials,
12 Water Tumblers
60 pieces $11 50

No. 4786

Glass Sets

Bohemian, plain; as follows:
12 Saucer Champs., 12 Round Bowl Clarets,
12 Wines, 12 Cordials,
12 Water Tumblers.
60 pieces $6 40

PRICE LIST—SEPARATE ARTICLES

Baccarat, Plain

Goblets	per doz.,	$3 10
Clarets, R. B.	"	2 75
Wines	"	2 60
Cordials	"	2 35
Sherries	"	3 10
Saucer Champs.	per doz.,	$3 10
Champ. Tumblers	"	1 35
Water Tumblers, large,	"	2 00
Water Tumblers, medium,	"	1 70
Whiskey Tumblers	"	1 35
Finger Bowls	per doz.,	$3 35
Finger Bowl Plates	"	5 75
Lemonades, handled	"	3 00
Spoon Holder	each,	80
Celery Glass	"	1 00

Cheese Dish, covered, large size . . each, $2 00 Cheese Dish, covered, small size . . each, $1 75

Bohemian, Plain

Goblets, large	per doz.,	$2 00
Clarets	"	1 70
Wines	"	1 40
Cordials	"	1 25
Sherries	"	1 90
Lemonades, handled	"	1 70
Saucer Champs.	per doz.,	$2 00
Champ. Tumblers	"	80
Water Tumblers	"	80
Whiskey Tumblers	"	60
Finger Bowls	"	2 00
Pint Decanters	each,	85
Quart Decanters	each,	$1 00
Pint Claret Jug	"	1 00
Quart Claret Jug	"	1 30
Oil Bottle	"	50
Water Bottle	"	95

GLASS SETS—Continued

No. 4787

Glass Set. No. 582–006

Empire wreath border decoration, engraved, as follows:

12 Saucer Champs.,
12 Clarets,
12 Wines,
12 Cordials,
12 Water Tumblers.

60 pieces $9 00

We also carry this line complete, prices of which we give herewith:

	Per doz.		Per doz.
Goblets	$2 70	Pousee Cafés	$2 00
Saucer Champs	2 70	Water Tumblers, large size	80
Champs., Tall	2 30	Champ. Tumblers . .	80
Clarets, R. B.	2 30	Whiskey Tumblers . .	70
Cocktails	2 30	Lemonades, handled .	2 40
Wines	2 20	Finger Bowls	3 00
Sherries	2 20	Egg Glasses, Ftd. . .	2 80
Cordials	2 00		

No. 4788

No. 561–4957—**Wine Set**

Green glass, rich gold decoration, solid gold handle decanter 16½ inches high, 6 glasses, complete on mirror tray . . . $12 25

Glasses separate, $12 00 dozen   Decanter . . . . $3 00 each

WHISKEY SETS

No. 4789

Whiskey Set—No. 7931

Etched design with gold cut neck and cut stopper. 1 decanter 6 whiskey glasses and 1 handled mirror tray, complete $10.00

No. 4790

Whiskey Set—No. 5533

Etched design. 1 whiskey jug, 6 whiskey glasses, 1 handled mirror tray, complete $5.25

CORDIAL SETS

No. 4791

Cordial Set—No. 269—Gold.

Rich etched design, filled with burnished gold on neck and stopper. 1 decanter, 6 cordial glasses. 1 handled mirror tray, complete $10.45

4792

Cordial Set—"Schiller"

Etched crystal glass. 1 cordial decanter, 6 cordial glasses, 1 handled mirror tray, complete $5.95

CORDIAL SETS—Continued

No. 4793

Cordial Set. "Optic"

1 decanter, 6 cordial glasses, 1 handled mirror tray, complete $5 70

No. 4794

No. 41411–4957—**Liquor Set**

Green glass, raised paste gold decoration and traced gold on stem, 6 glasses, decanter on handled mirror tray, $8 70

LIQUOR SETS, CHAMPAGNE GLASSES

No. 4795

No. 31411–2657—**Liquor Set**

Ruby glass with raised gold decoration, solid gold handle, flange shape glasses, **6 glasses**, decanter on mirror tray, complete $6 45

No. 4796

No. 272–6621—**Tall Champagne**

Raised paste gold decoration on bowl and foot, twisted stem, 9½ inches high, per dozen . . . $57 00

Sold singly at same rate.

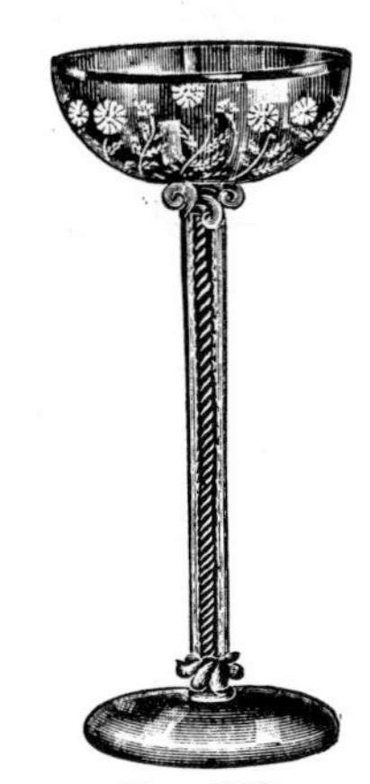

No. 4797

No. 871–948—**Tall Champagne**

Cut and gold flower decoration on bowl and foot, ruby cut stem, 9½ inches high, per dozen $66 00

Sold separately at same rate.

RHINE WINE OR HOCK GLASSES—Bohemian Glass

No. 4798

Rhine Wine Glass

Raised gold lace work, solid gold edges, and gold line on foot. In rose and green.

No. 982-I, 2693, per doz., $19 05

No. 4799

Liquor and Cordial Glass

Heavy raised gold decoration, gold edge and gold line on foot, in rose or green colored glass.

No. 3-0655 . . per doz., $6 05

No. 4800

Rhine Wine or Hock Glass

Raised gold decoration throughout, solid gold edge and heavy gold line on foot. In either rose or green colored glass.

No. 475-0655 . per doz., $27 20

No. 4801

Liquor or Cordial Glass

Flower decoration in gold. heavy gold edge, and heavy gold line on foot. In rose or green colored glass.

No. 5001-4554 . per doz., $11 30

No. 4802

Rhine Wine or Hock Glass

Heavy raised gold decoration, solid gold edge, and heavy gold line on foot; cut stem. Bowl delicate green.

No. 7342-9555 . per doz., $49 85

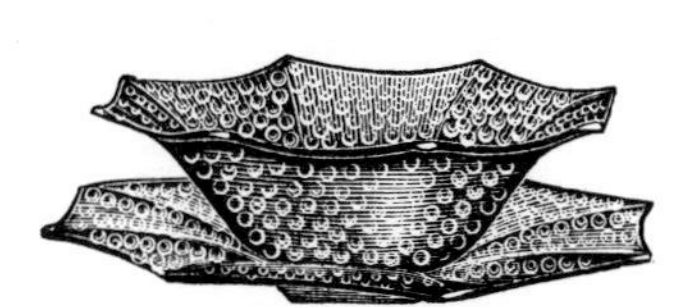

No. 4803

Finger Bowl and Plate

With raised gold lace work, and solid gold edges. In either rose, green or blue.

No. 158-2693 . per doz., $42 30

No. 4804

Roman Punch or Sherbet Glass, with Saucer

Decorated in raised gold, with gold edge, solid gold handle, In either green or rose color.

No. 251-0655 . per doz., $21 70

No. 4805

Bon Bon on Foot

2½ in. high 5½ in. across, raised gold lace work decoration, solid gold edge. In either, rose, green or heliotrope glass.

No. 7733-2693 . . each, $2 60

No. 4806

Roman Punch or Sherbet Glass

Assorted delicate colors, raised gold decoration.

Per doz. $9 50

No. 4807

Bon Bon, with Plate

Also nice for sherbet. Raised gold lace work. Solid gold edges. In either green or rose.

No. 117-2693 . each, $3 90

CANDELABRUM CANDLESTICKS AND VASES

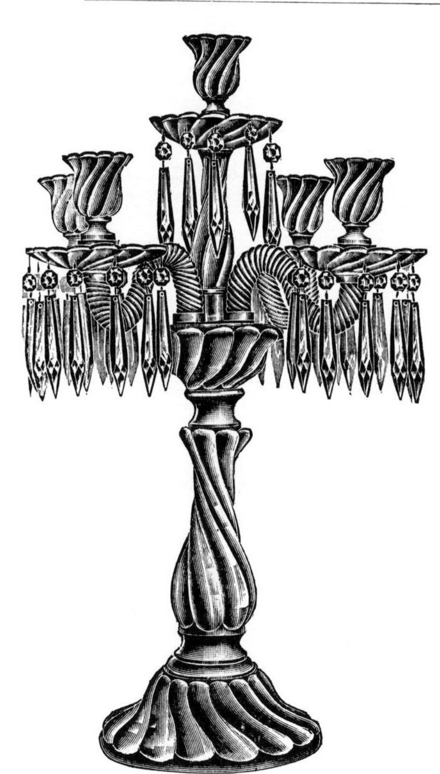

No. 4808

Crystal Glass Candelabra

No. 7, 5-light, 23¼ inches high, each, $8 50

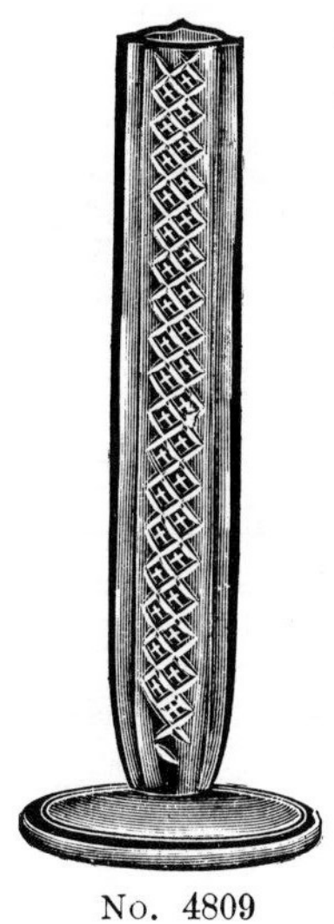

No. 4809

Cut Glass Flower Vase—No. 8252

Gold line on top and on foot; also on three sides.

In.	Price	In.	Price
4	$0 30	12	$1 50
5	0 40	14	2 00
6	0 55	16	2 75
8	0 80	18	3 50
10	1 20	20	4 25

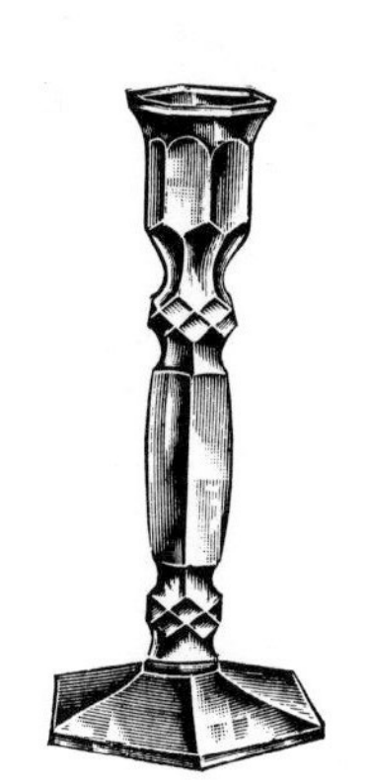

No. 4810

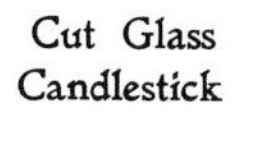

Cut Glass Candlestick

8½ inches high
Each, $1 75

10½ inches high
Each, $3 00

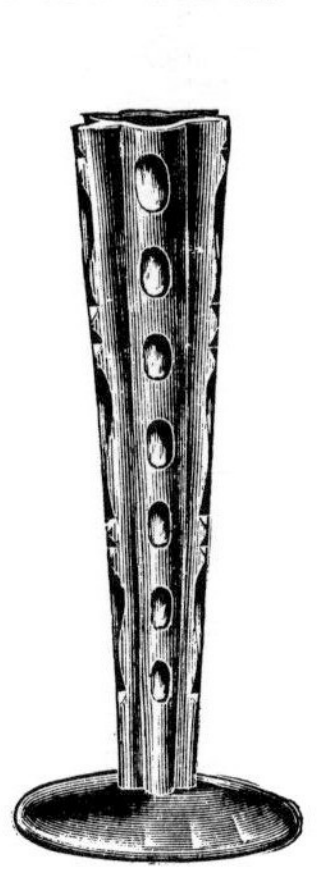

No. 4811

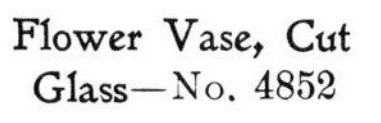

Flower Vase, Cut Glass—No. 4852

In.	Price	In.	Price
4	$0 25	12	$1 10
5	0 30	14	1 40
6	0 40	16	1 85
8	0 55	18	2 25
10	0 75	20	2 75

No. 4812

Crystal Candelabra

No. 2, 4-light, 19¼ inches high each, $5 30

STEM WARE AND SILVER-MOUNTED CUT GLASS

DINNER WARE

Covered Dish

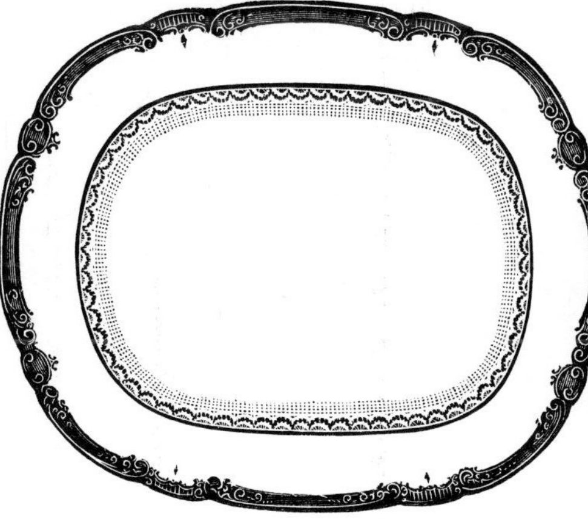

Dish

Sauce Tureen

Plate

No. 4813

No. 8729 G—**English Minton China**

Border decoration in English Lacquer or Maroon, outlined by gold and fancy gold lace design on shoulder of plate and handles. All in best burnished clouded gold. Can be had in any quantity desired, and matched at any time.

Prices of single pieces mailed on application, estimates furnished.

127 pieces, complete	$404.00
100 " "	329.50
Soup Set	91.20
Salad Set	52.00

For Actual Colors see Colored Insert C, following page 100

Cup and Saucer

DINNER WARE—Continued

For Actual Colors see Colored insert G, following page 164

Covered Dish

Sauce Tureen

Dish. No. 4814

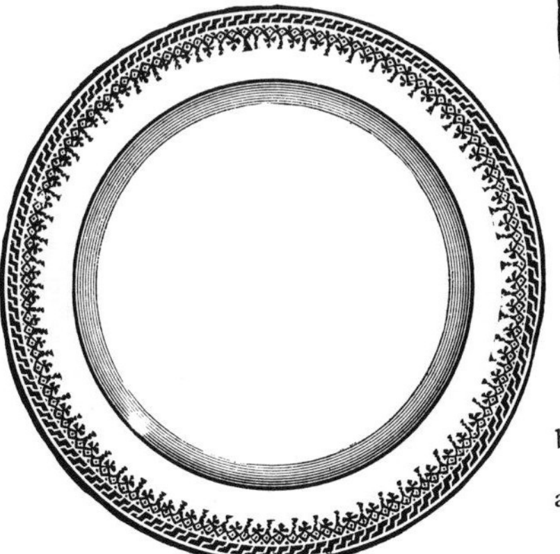

Plate

No. 5954—English Wedgwood China

Cream border with etched gold and fancy gold lace border, handles stippled gold.

Can be bought in any quantity desired, and matched at any time. Estimates promptly furnished.

127 pieces, complete	$262 90
100 " "	215 00
Soup Set	50 70
Salad Set	37 50

Cup and Saucer

Covered Dish

DINNER WARE

Continued

For Actual Colors see Colored Insert D,
following page 122

Sauce Tureen

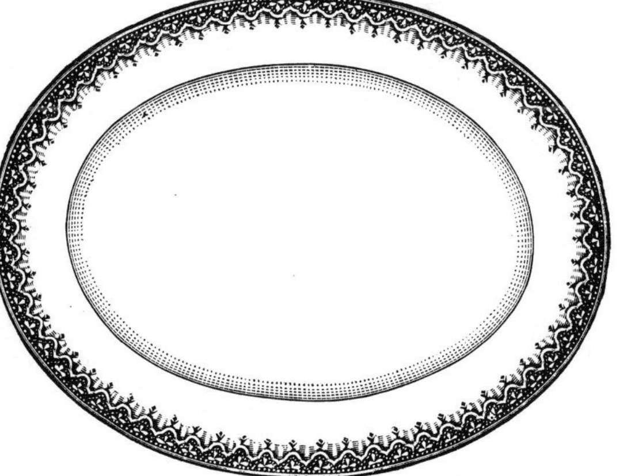

Dish. No. 4815

Plate

No. x2674—**Wedgwood English China**

Border decoration in underglazed dark blue, gold edges, gold lace inside blue border, gold sunray handles.

Can be bought in any quantity desired, and matched at any time. Estimates promptly furnished.

127 pieces, complete,	$218 80	Soup Set	$42 90
100 " "	180 75	Salad Set	30 55
56 " Tea Set .	58 25		

Cup and Saucer

DINNER WARE—Continued

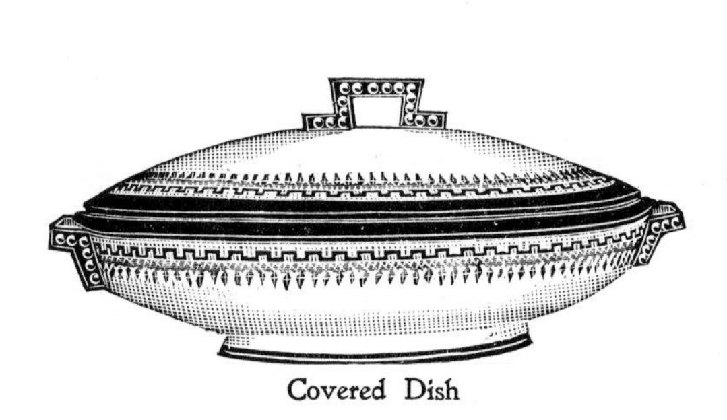

Covered Dish

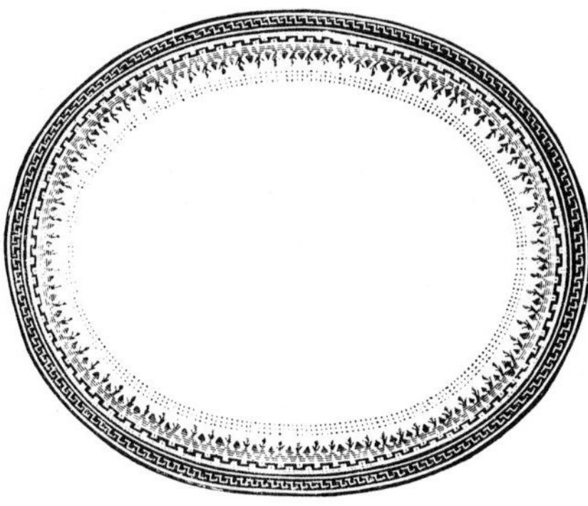

Dish

Sauce Tureen

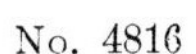

No. 4816

Plate

No. 3178 H—**English Cauldon China**

Three lines of scoured gold on edge with key border decoration on center band in black, and hair brown border extending toward center of plate.

Can be bought in any quantity desired, and matched at any time. Prices of single pieces mailed on application. Estimates furnished.

127 pieces, complete	$205 00
100 " "	168 00
Soup Set	41 80
Salad Set	27 95

For Actual Colors see Colored Insert C, following page 100

Cup and Saucer

DINNER WARE—Continued

Covered Dish

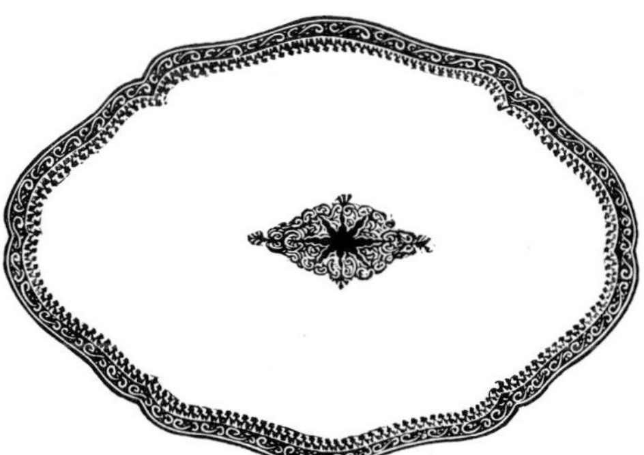
Dish

Sauce Tureen

No. 4817

No. 343—**White and Gold Incrustation**

Finest Limoges China, with incrusted gold border decoration, with lace border extending toward center, and fancy gold rosette center.

Can be bought in any quantity desired, and matched at any time. Prices of single pieces mailed on application. Estimates furnished.

127 pieces, complete	$220 50
100 " "	178 90
Soup Set	37 65
Salad Set	28 95

Plate

Cup and Saucer

For Actual Colors see Colored Insert A, following page 78

DINNER WARE—Continued

Covered Dish

Dish

Sauce Tureen

No. 4818

No. 952—**Limoges China**

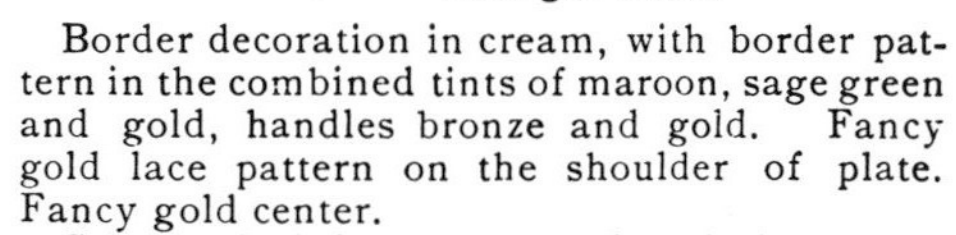

Border decoration in cream, with border pattern in the combined tints of maroon, sage green and gold, handles bronze and gold. Fancy gold lace pattern on the shoulder of plate. Fancy gold center.

Can be had in any quantity desired, and matched at any time. Prices of single pieces mailed on application. Estimates furnished.

127 pieces, complete	$170 60
100 " "	134 80
Soup Set	30 60
Salad Set	22 50

Cup and Saucer

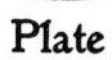

Plate

For Actual Colors see Colored Insert G, following page 164

DINNER WARE—Continued

Covered Dish

Dish

Sauce Boat

No. 4819

No. 2912—**English Wedgwood China**

Border flower decoration in delicate pink and yellow flowers, green and gold leaves. Also heavily decorated with best burnished gold throughout.

This set can be bought in any quantity desired, and matched at any time. Estimates promptly furnished.

127 pieces, complete	$262 90
100 " "	215 00
56-piece Tea Set	73 70
Soup Set	50 70
Salad Set	37 50

Plate

Cup and Saucer

For Actual Colors see Colored Insert F, following page 154

DINNER WARE—Continued

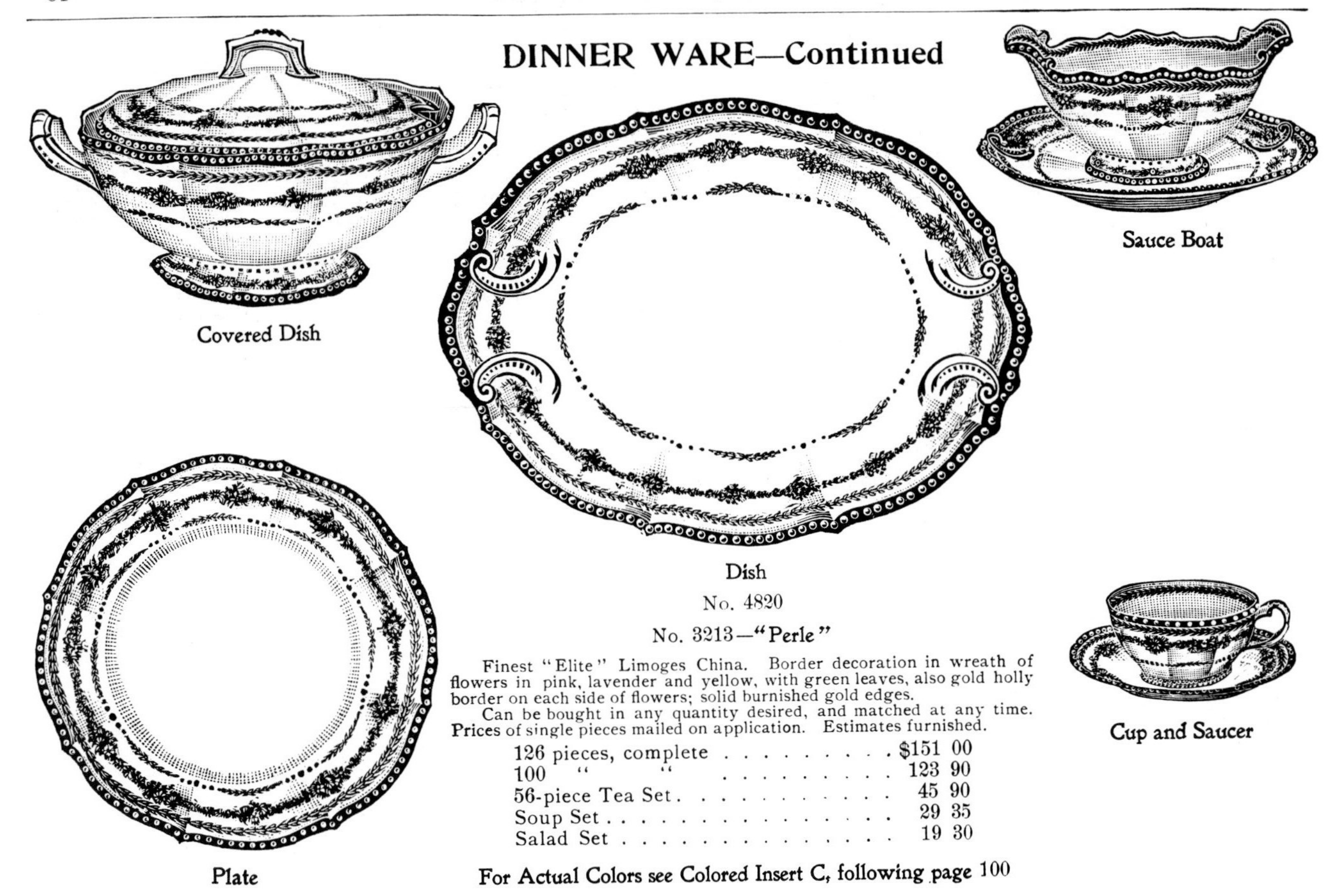

Covered Dish

Sauce Boat

Dish

Plate

Cup and Saucer

No. 4820

No. 3213—"Perle"

Finest "Elite" Limoges China. Border decoration in wreath of flowers in pink, lavender and yellow, with green leaves, also gold holly border on each side of flowers; solid burnished gold edges.

Can be bought in any quantity desired, and matched at any time. Prices of single pieces mailed on application. Estimates furnished.

126 pieces, complete	$151 00
100 " "	123 90
56-piece Tea Set	45 90
Soup Set	29 35
Salad Set	19 30

For Actual Colors see Colored Insert C, following page 100

DINNER WARE

Continued

For Actual Colors see Colored Insert A, following page 78

Covered Dish

Sauce Tureen

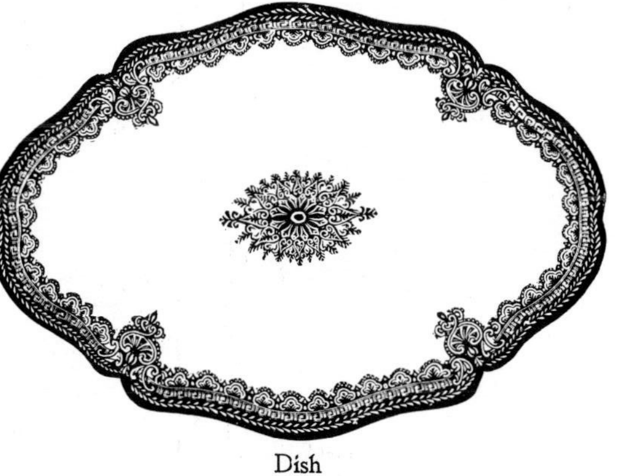

Plate

Dish

No. 4821

No. 9872—"**Argent**"

Finest Limoges China, with gold lace border, gold edge, solid burnished gold handles.

Can be bought in any quantity desired, and matched at any time. Prices of single pieces mailed on application. Estimates furnished.

127 pieces, complete	$148 50
100 " "	121 50
56-piece Tea Set	45 65
Soup Set	25 95
Salad Set	18 75

Cup and Saucer

DINNER WARE—Continued

Covered Dish

Dish
No. 4822

Sauce Tureen

No. 197-84—"Turgot"

Finest "Elite" Limoges China, cream body border, with two rows of burnished gold, and very delicate green tint between the gold. Fancy gold star center.

Can he bought in any quantity desired, and matched at any time. Prices of single pieces mailed on application. Estimates furnished.

126 pieces, complete	$143 75
100 " "	115 00
56-piece Tea Set	47 75
Soup Set	26 30
Salad Set	18 55

For Actual Colors see Colored Insert G, following page 164

Plate

Cup and Saucer

DINNER WARE—Continued

Covered Dish

Dish

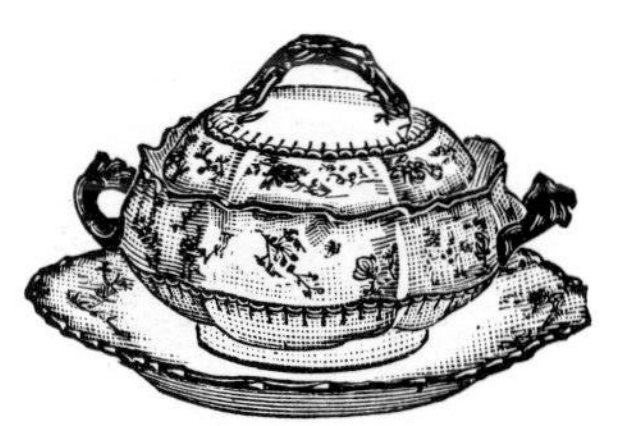

Sauce Tureen

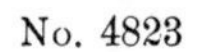

No. 4823

Plate

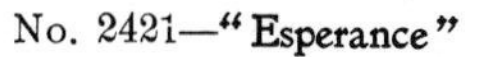

No. 2421—**"Esperance"**

Finest "Elite" Limoges China, border decoration of flowers in raised gold, solid gold handles and heavy burnished gold edges.

Can be bought in any quantity desired, and matched at any time. Estimates furnished.

127 pieces, complete	$131 10
100 " "	106 62
56-piece Tea Set	45 30
Soup Set	22 00
Salad Set	15 80

For Actual Colors see Colored Insert A, following page 78

Cup and Saucer

DINNER WARE—Continued

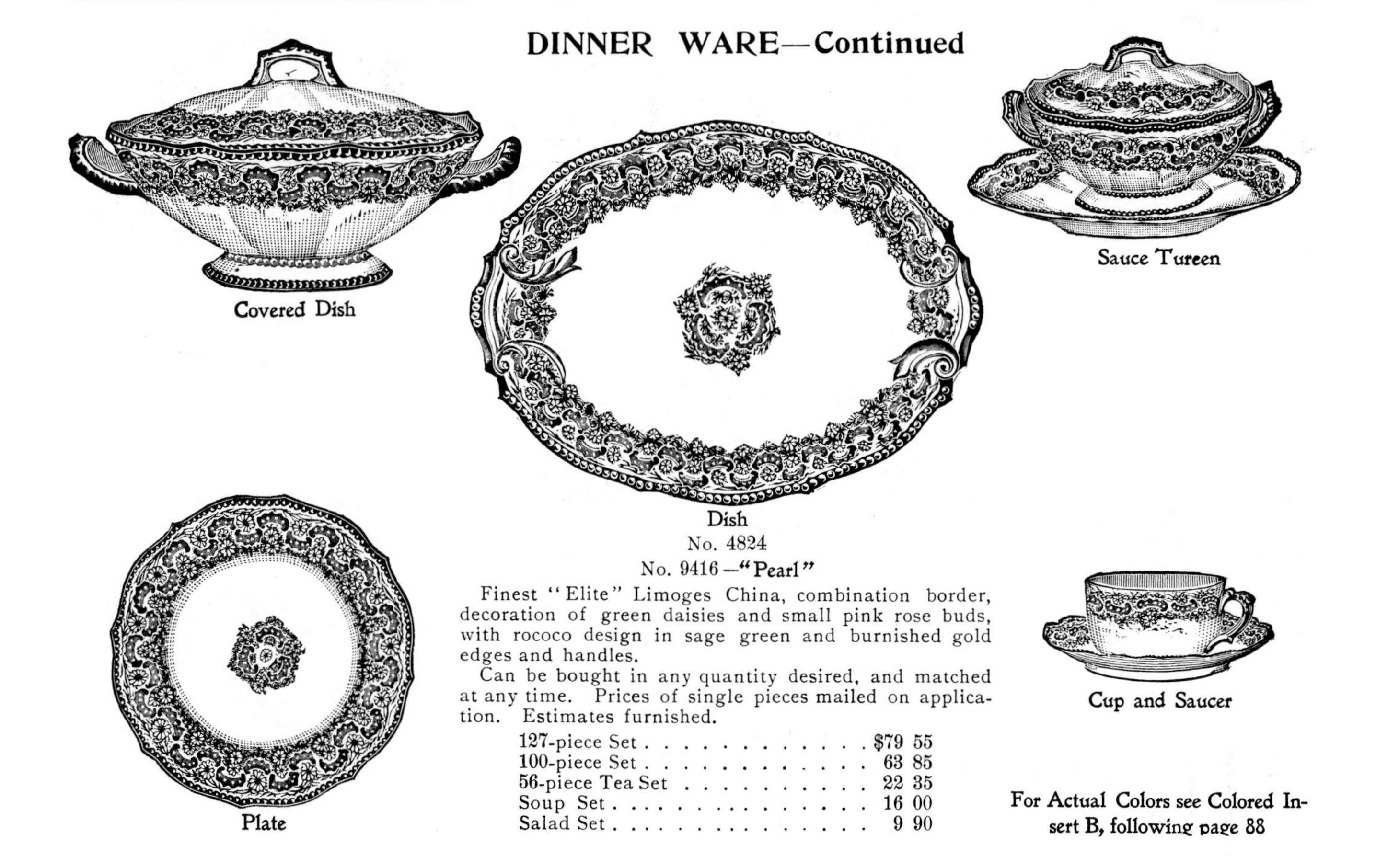

Covered Dish

Sauce Tureen

Dish

Plate

Cup and Saucer

No. 4824

No. 9416—**"Pearl"**

Finest "Elite" Limoges China, combination border, decoration of green daisies and small pink rose buds, with rococo design in sage green and burnished gold edges and handles.

Can be bought in any quantity desired, and matched at any time. Prices of single pieces mailed on application. Estimates furnished.

127-piece Set	$79 55
100-piece Set	63 85
56-piece Tea Set	22 35
Soup Set	16 00
Salad Set	9 90

For Actual Colors see Colored Insert B, following page 88

DINNER WARE—Continued

Covered Dish

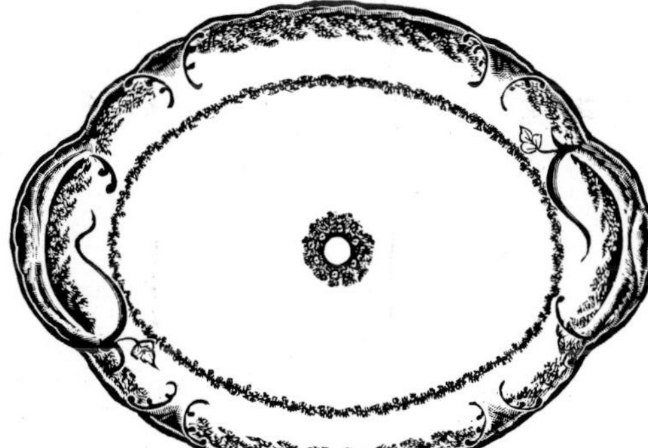

No. 4825

Dish

Sauce Tureen

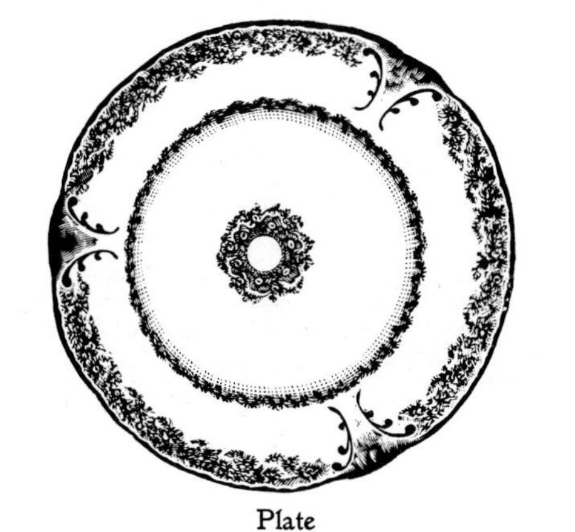

Plate

No. 2682—"St. Germain"

Haviland's finest Limoges China. Border decoration in delicate green flowers, with hair brown and lavender edge. Border of small flowers on shoulder of plate, and fancy rosette center. Clouded burnished gold edges and stippled gold handles.

Can be bought in any quantity desired and matched at any time. Prices of single pieces mailed on application. Estimates furnished.

127 pieces, complete	$88 40
100 " "	73 00
56-piece Tea Set	27 80
Soup Set	16 35
Salad Set	11 55

Cup and Saucer

For Actual Colors see Colored Insert D, following page 122

DINNER WARE—Continued

Covered Dish

No. 3424—"Marie Antoinette"

Haviland's Limoges China. Border decoration in bouquets of flowers in pink, blue, and sage green leaves, connecting vines of blue flowers and green leaves, gold stippled handles and panels of gold lace on edge. Can be bought in any quantity desired, and matched at any time. Estimates furnished.

Sauce Tureen

Plate

No. 4826

Dish

Cup and Saucer

127 pieces, complete	$73 50
100 " "	61 40
56-piece Tea Set	22 90
Soup Set	13 75
Salad Set	9 05

DINNER WARE—Continued

Covered Dish

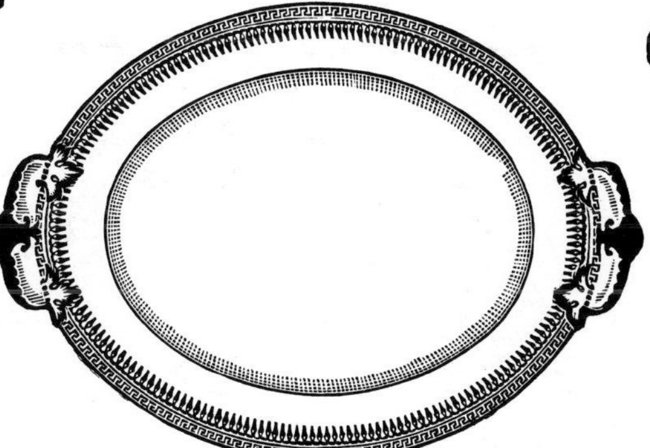

Dish

Sauce Tureen

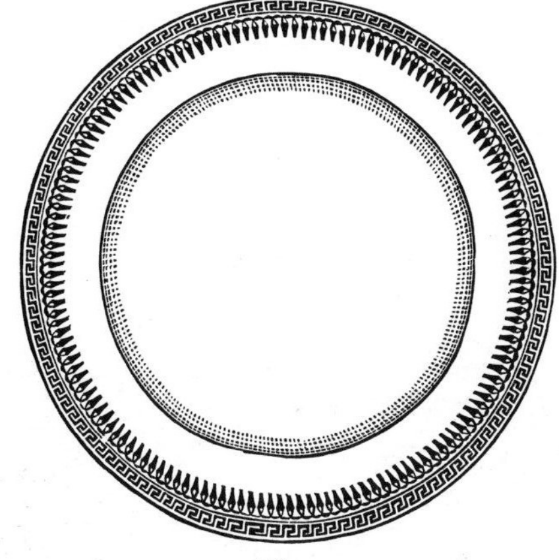

Plate

No. 4827

No. 049—**Limoges China**

Hair brown decoration. Burnished line of gold on edge, also shoulder of plate. This Set has the English shape plate as shown in the cut. Can be had in any quantity desired, and matched at any time. Prices of single pieces mailed on application. Estimates furnished.

126 pieces, complete	$68.50
100 " "	56.25
56-piece Tea Set	24.00
Soup Set	13.30
Salad Set	8.60

For Actual Colors see Colored Insert G, following page 164

Cup and Saucer

DINNER WARE—Continued

FINEST ELITE LIMOGES CHINA

For Actual Colors see Colored Insert F, following page 154

Covered Dish

Sauce Tureen

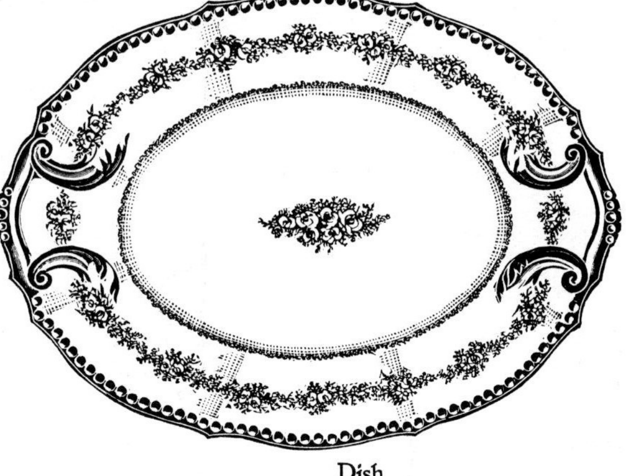

Dish

No. 4828

Plate

Cup and Saucer

No.0603—"Pearl"

Border decoration in small bouquets of pink and yellow flowers connected with small sprays of blue forget-me-nots. Burnished gold edges, and small wreath of flowers in sage green on shoulder of plates, etc. Can be bought in any quantity desired, and matched at any time. Prices of single pieces mailed on application. Estimates furnished.

126 pieces, complete $63.10
100 " " 51.60
56-piece Tea Set $20.00
Soup Set 12.15
Salad Set $7.95

DINNER WARE—Continued

Covered Dish

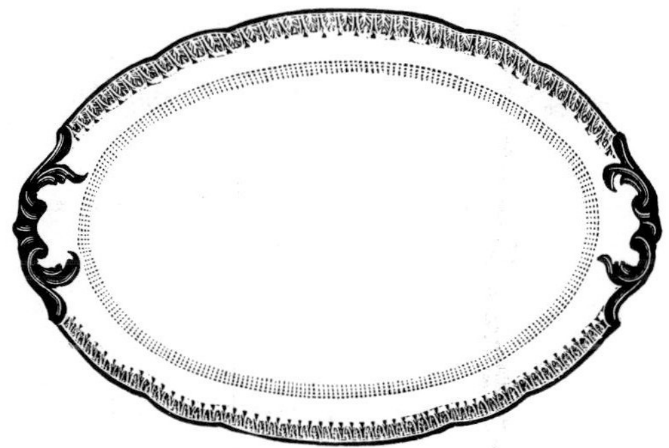

Dish

Sauce Tureen

No. 4829

No. 7843—"Napoleon"

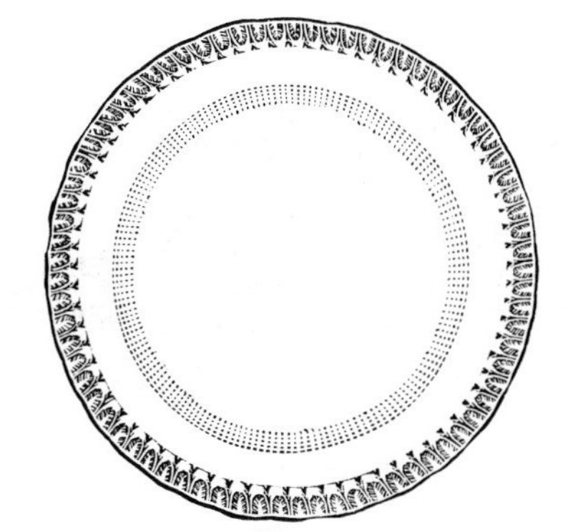

Plate

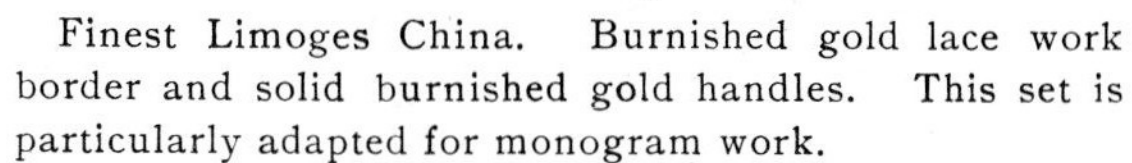

Finest Limoges China. Burnished gold lace work border and solid burnished gold handles. This set is particularly adapted for monogram work.

Can be bought in any quantity desired, and matched at any time. Prices of single pieces mailed on application. Estimates furnished.

127 pieces, complete	$63 15
113 " "	52 00
56-piece Tea Set	21 00
Soup Set	12 40
Salad Set	8 25

Cup and Saucer

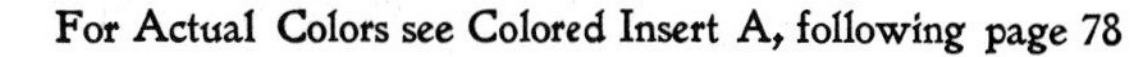

For Actual Colors see Colored Insert A, following page 78

DINNER WARE—Continued

Covered Dish

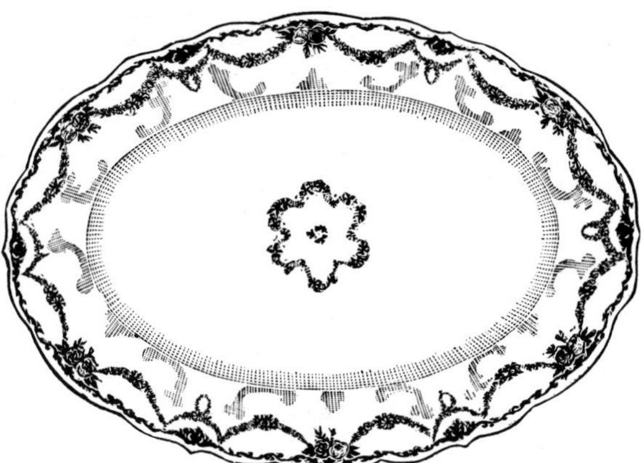

Sauce Tureen

Dish

No. 4830

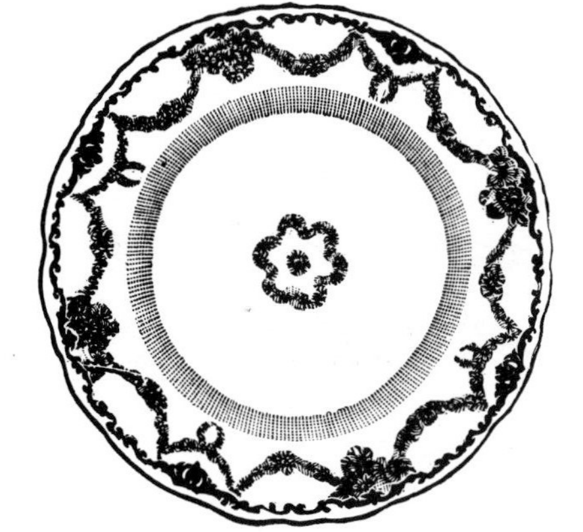

Plate

Cup and Saucer

No. D-279—"Navarre"

Finest Limoges China, border decoration in festoon and garlands of delicate pink, yellow and blue flowers, green leaves. Sage green and rococo border. Rosette center of flowers.

The combination and blending of the colors in this decoration is particularly delicate and very handsome.

Can be bought in any quantity desired and matched at any time. Prices of single pieces mailed on application. Estimates furnished.

126 pieces, complete	$54 15
100 " "	44 20
56-piece Tea Set	17 30
Soup Set	10 00
Salad Set	6 65

For Actual Colors see Colored Insert A, following page 78

DINNER WARE—Continued

Covered Dish

Sauce Tureen

Dish

No. 4831

Cup and Saucer

Plate

No. 7159—"Napoleon"

Finest Limoges China, with a green empire wreath, and festoon border, green lace work and gold lines on shoulder of plate. Solid burnished gold handles. Can be had in any quantity desired, and matched at any time. Prices of single pieces mailed on application. Estimates furnished.

126 pieces, complete	$53 50	Soup Set	$9 95
100 " "	44 00	Salad Set	6 40
56-piece Tea Set . .	18 20		

For Actual Colors see Colored Insert D, following page 122

DINNER WARE—Continued

Covered Dish

Sauce Tureen

Dish

No. 4832

Plate

No. 8765—**Brown Arabesque**

Finest Limoges China. Scroll border decoration in hair brown, with gold edge and gold traced handles. Can be bought in any quantity desired, and matched at any time. Prices of single pieces mailed on application. Estimates furnished.

126 pieces, complete	$52 95
100 " "	42 60
55-piece Tea Set (no Bowl)	15 75
Soup Set	9 90
Salad Set	6 15

For Actual Colors see Colored Insert G, following page 164

Cup and Saucer

DINNER WARE—Continued

For Actual Colors see Colored Insert F, following page 154

Covered Dish

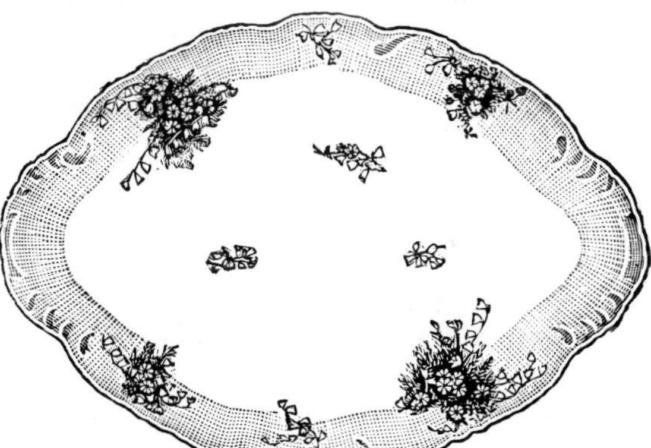

Dish

Sauce Tureen

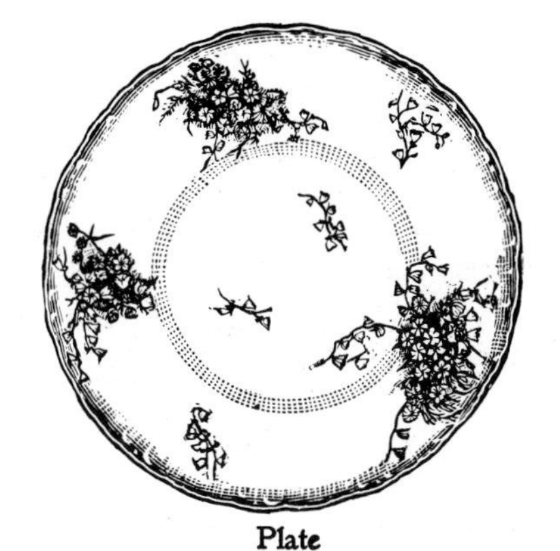

Plate

No. 4833

No. 3962 A—"Rouen"

Haviland finest Limoges China. Decorated with trailing arbutus in delicate pink, with background of maidenhair fern in light green, small sprays being scattered artistically over each piece ; handles clouded burnished gold.

Can be bought in any quantity desired, and matched at any time. Prices of single pieces mailed on application. Estimates furnished.

126 pieces, complete	$47 50
100 " "	38 00
56-piece Tea Set	14 90
Soup Set	8 00
Salad Set	4 90

Cup and Saucer

DINNER WARE—Continued

For Actual Colors see Colored Insert C, following page 100

Covered Dish

Dish

Sauce Tureen

Plate

No. 4834

Haviland finest Limoges China. Decorated with Morning Glories in delicate combined tints of blue, pink and yellow, and green leaves; handles clouded gold. Can be bought in any quantity desired, and matched at any time. Prices of single pieces mailed on application. Estimates furnished.

127 pieces	$41 50
100 "	34 50
56-piece Tea Set	12 60
Soup Set	7 85
Salad Set	5 25

Cup and Saucer

DINNER WARE

(Continued)

Covered Dish

Sauce Tureen

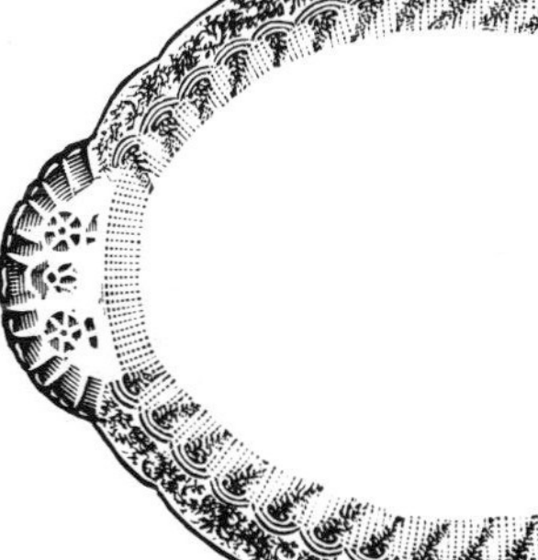

Dish

No. 4835

Plate

No. 8767—**"Columbia"**

Finest Limoges China. Border decoration delicate yellow flowers and green sprays, with burnished gold handles.

Can be bought in any quantity desired, and matched at any time. Prices of single pieces mailed on application. Estimates furnished.

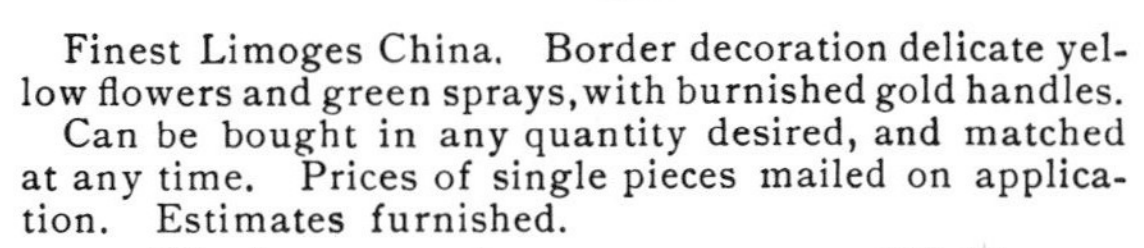

126 pieces, complete	$45 95
100 " "	37 15
56-piece Tea Set	13 90
Soup Set	8 60
Salad Set	5 00

Cup and Saucer

DINNER WARE
(Continued)

Covered Dish

Sauce Boat

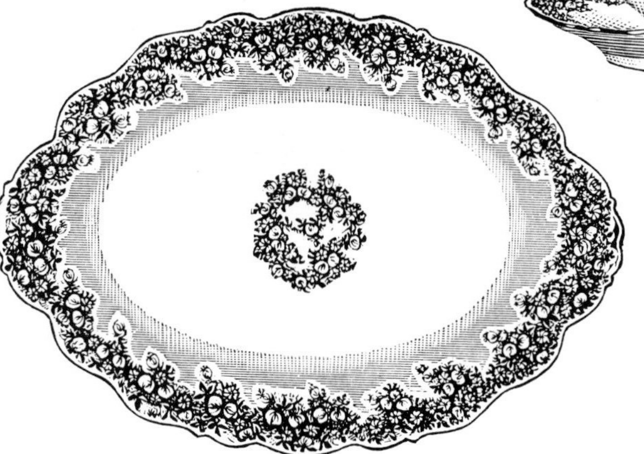

Dish
No 4836

Plate

Cup and Saucer

No. 1516—**"Odette"**

Dinner Set, Elite Limoges China. Border decoration in festoons of pink, purple and sage green flowers with light green leaves; fancy center in same colors.

Can be bought in any quantity desired, and matched at any time. Prices of single pieces mailed on application. Estimates furnished.

127 pieces, complete	$33 00
100 " "	27 35
56-piece Tea Set	9 35
Soup Set	6 50
Salad Set	4 00

Covered Dish

DINNER WARE

(Continued)

For Actual Colors see Colored Insert F, following page 154

Sauce Tureen

Dish

No. 4837

Cup and Saucer

Plate

No. 4128—"**Louvre**"

Limoges Elite China. Border decoration of roses in pink with sage green leaves, each piece clouded burnished gold edge; clouded gold handles.

Can be bought in any quantity desired, and matched at any time. Estimates furnished.

127 pieces, complete	$47.50	56-piece Tea Set	$13.65
100 " "	39.00	Soup Set	9.00

Salad Set $5.60

DINNER WARE—Continued

Covered Dish

Sauce Tureen

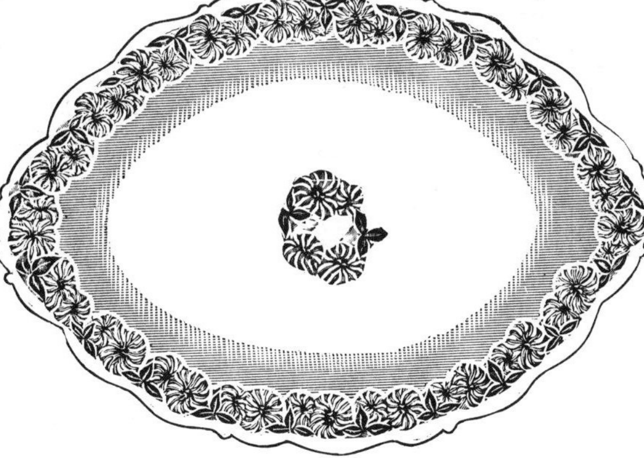

Dish

Plate

No. 4838

No. 5628—**"Odette"**

Limoges "Elite" China. Border decoration of morning glories in purple, with sage green leaves, on delicate background of yellow.

102 pieces, complete $27.50

Cup and Saucer

DINNER WARE—Continued

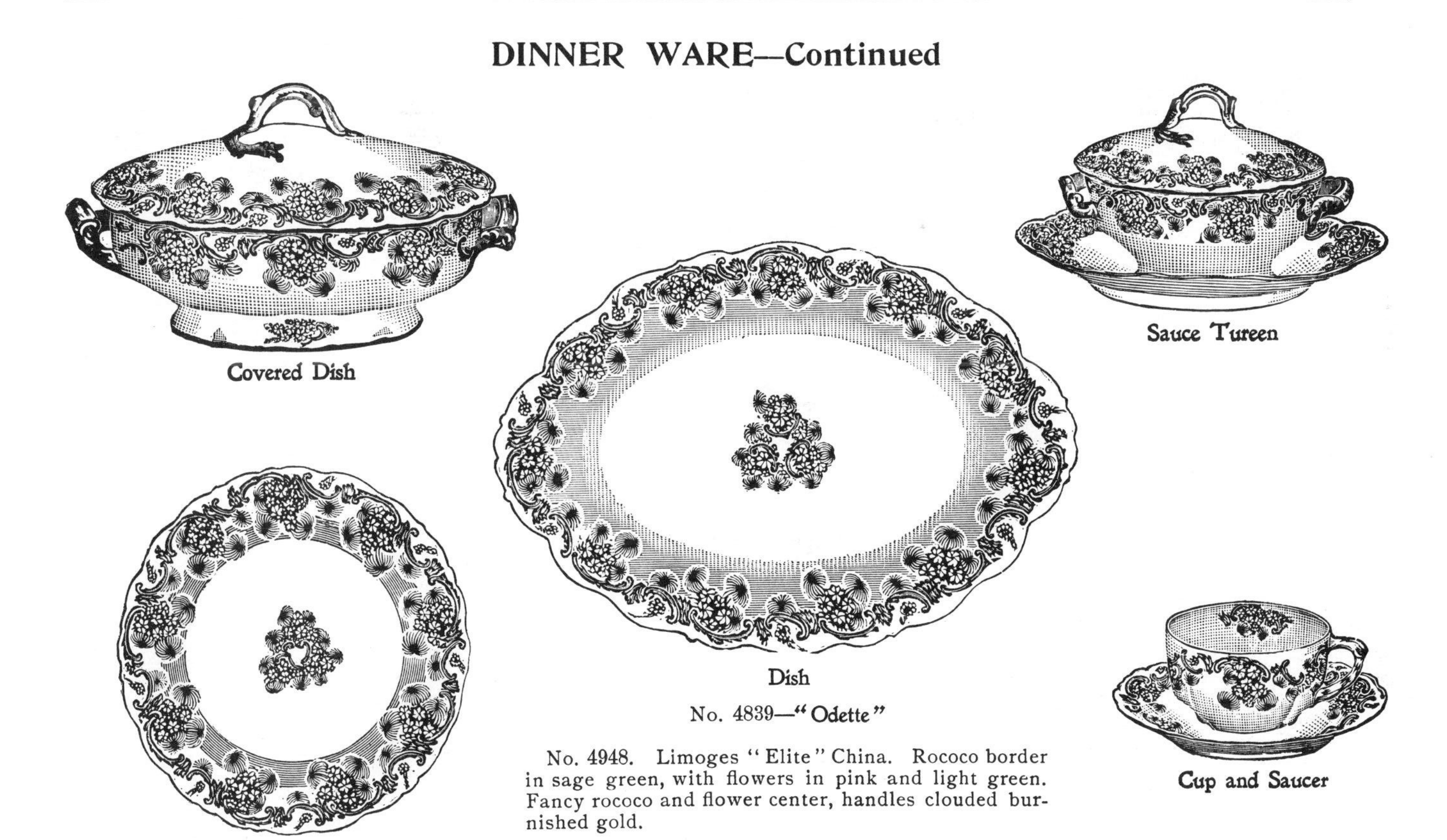

Covered Dish

Sauce Tureen

Dish

No. 4839—"Odette"

Plate

Cup and Saucer

No. 4948. Limoges "Elite" China. Rococo border in sage green, with flowers in pink and light green. Fancy rococo and flower center, handles clouded burnished gold.

102 pieces, complete $27 50

DINNER WARE

Continued

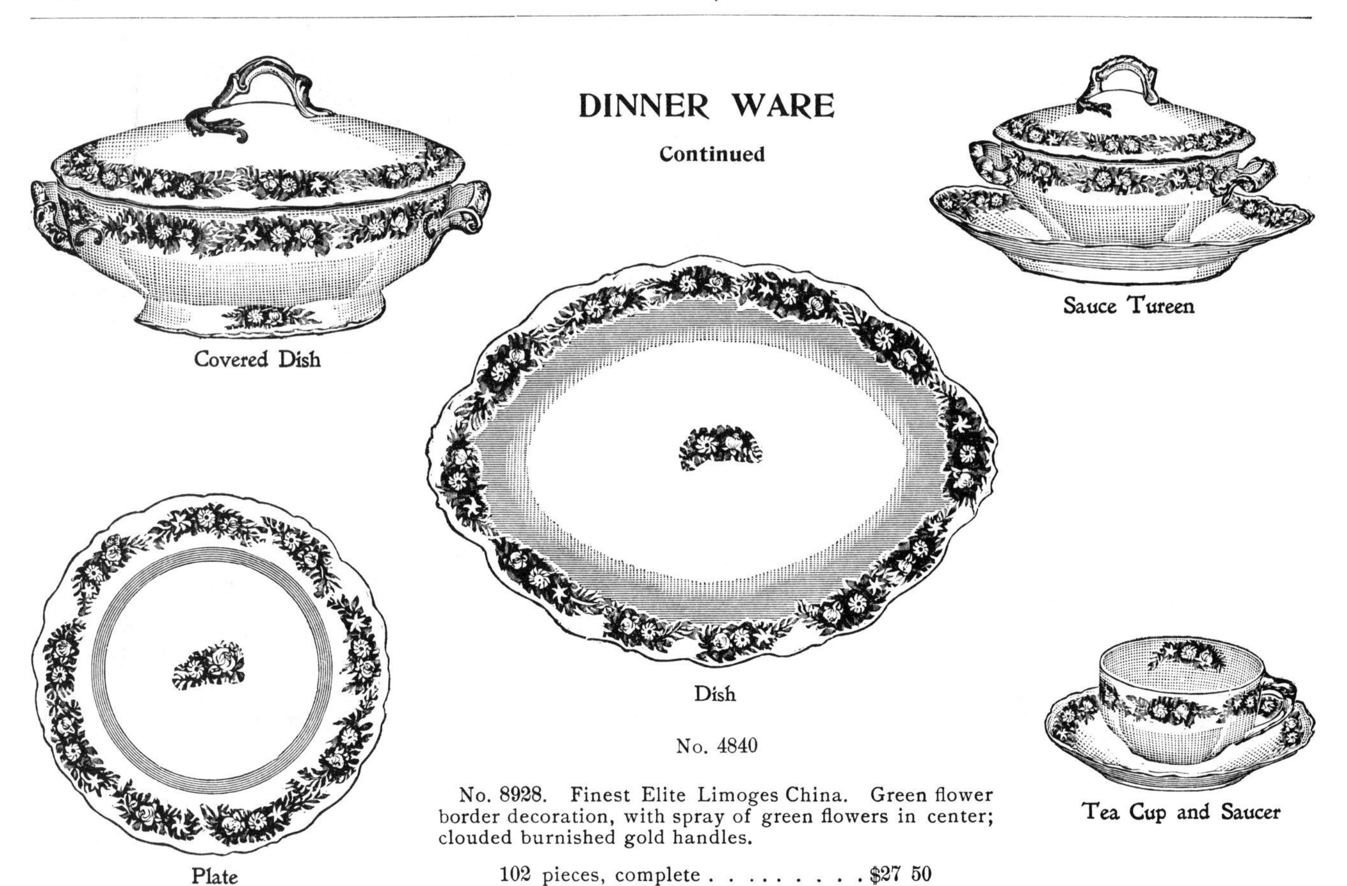

Covered Dish

Sauce Tureen

Dish

Plate

Tea Cup and Saucer

No. 4840

No. 8928. Finest Elite Limoges China. Green flower border decoration, with spray of green flowers in center; clouded burnished gold handles.

102 pieces, complete $27 50

Covered Dish

DINNER WARE—Continued

For Actual Colors see Colored Insert F, following page 154

Sauce Tureen

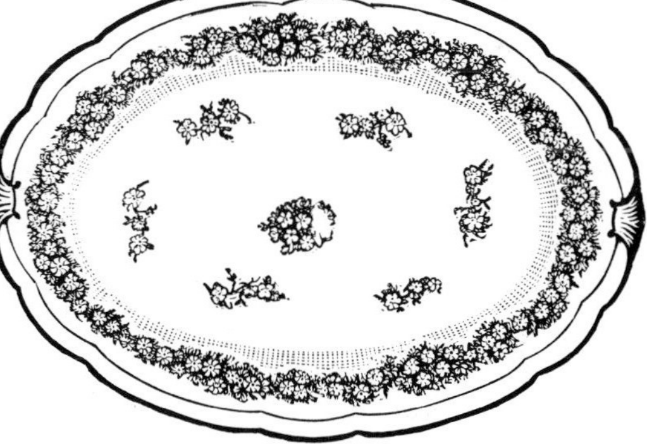

Dish

No. 4841

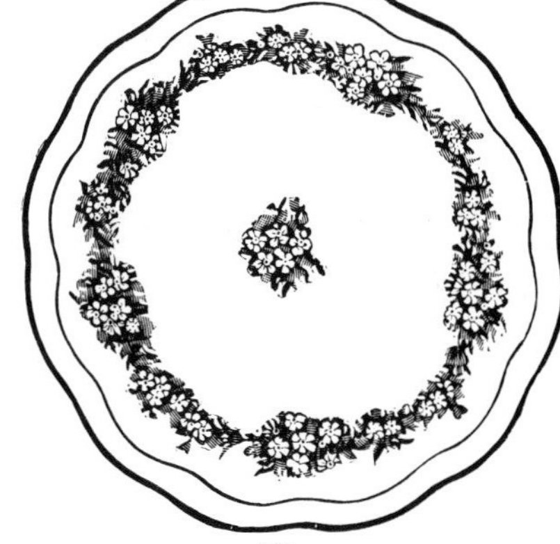

Plate

No. 289-B—CARLSBAD DINNER WARE

Border decoration of delicate blue flowers, green background, gold edge, gold traced handles.

Can be bought in any quantity desired, and matched at any time. Prices on single pieces mailed on application. Estimates furnished.

127 pieces, complete, $28 50   56-piece Tea Set . $8 00
100 " " 23 25   Soup Set. 5 75
Salad Set $2 70

Cup and Saucer

DINNER WARE

(Continued)

Composition of 102-piece Dinner Sets as shown on this and preceding page

12 Dinner Plates
12 Tea Plates
12 Soup Plates
12 Fruit Saucers
12 Individual Butters
1 10-inch Dish
1 12-inch Dish
1 16-inch Dish
1 Comport
1 Soup Tureen
1 Sauce Boat and Stand
2 Covered Vegetable Dishes
2 Uncovered Vegetable Dishes
1 Pickle
1 Covered Butter
12 Tea Cups and Saucers

No. 4842. Dinner Set, finest Limoges China, No. 3277. Green spray decoration in two shades of green, clouded stippled gold handles.

102 pieces, complete $25 00

No. 4843. Dinner Set, finest Limoges China, No. 7377, large rose decoration in natural color, light blue and sage green leaves; stippled gold handles.

102 pieces, complete. . . . $25 00

No. 4842

No. 4843

DINNER WARE—Continued

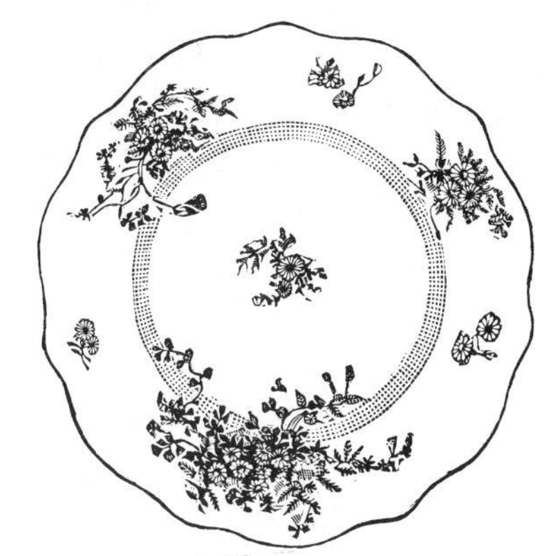

No. 4844

No. 4844. Dinner Set. Finest Limoges China, No. 1467. Decorated with flowers in spray decoration with delicate blue and green leaves; smaller flowers being artistically scattered over the entire surface. Stippled gold handles.

102 pieces, complete . $25 00

No. 4845. Dinner Set. Finest Limoges China, No. 3767. Bouquet decoration of flowers in pink, yellow and light blue, with sage green leaves; stippled gold handles.

102 pieces, complete . $25 00

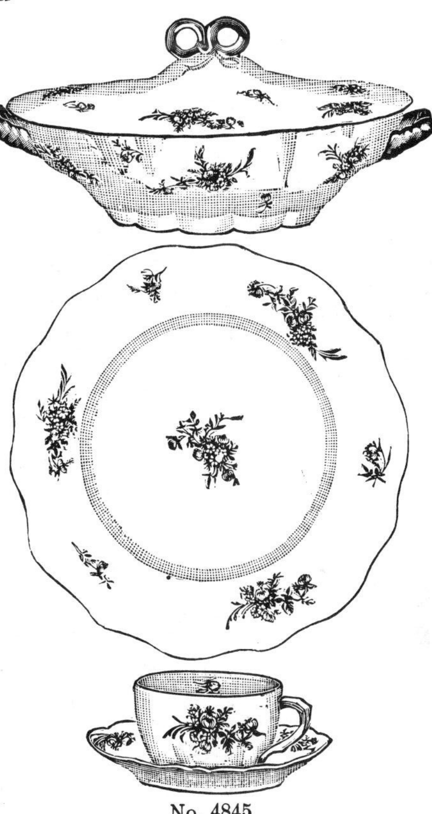

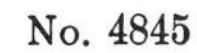

No. 4845

DINNER WARE
(Continued)

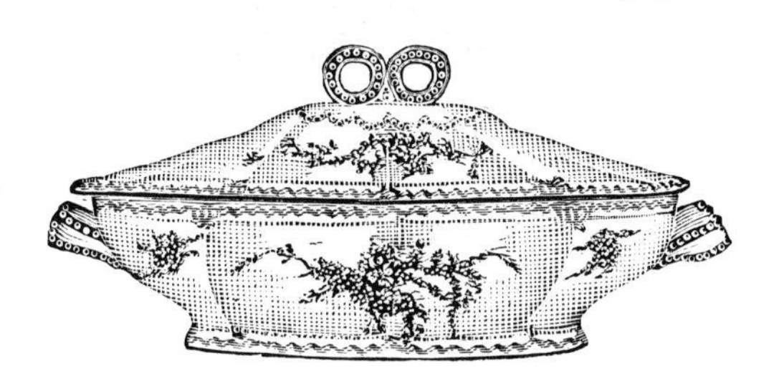

Composition of 102-Piece Dinner Sets as shown on this page

12 Dinner Plates
12 Tea Plates
12 Soup Plates
12 Fruit Saucers
12 Individual Butters
1 10-inch Dish
1 12-inch Dish
1 16-inch Dish
1 Comport
1 Soup Tureen
1 Sauce Boat and Stand
2 Covered Vegetable Dishes
2 Uncovered Vegetable Dishes
1 Pickle
1 Covered Butter
12 Tea Cups and Saucers

No. 4846. Haviland finest Limoges China. Embossed ribbon border with artistic spray decoration in blue and pink flowers, with sage green leaves.

102 pieces, complete . $25 00

No. 4847. Haviland finest Limoges China. Embossed ribbon border with spray of flowers in heliotrope, with sage green leaves.

102 pieces, complete . $25 00

No. 4846

No. 4847

DINNER WARE
(Continued)

Composition of 102-Piece Dinner Sets as shown on this page

12 Dinner Plates
12 Tea Plates
12 Soup Plates
12 Fruit Saucers
12 Individual Butters
1 10-inch Dish
1 12-inch Dish
1 16-inch Dish
1 Comport
1 Soup Tureen
1 Sauce Boat and Stand
2 Covered Vegetable Dishes
2 Uncovered Vegetable Dishes
1 Pickle
1 Covered Butter
12 Tea Cups and Saucers

No. 4848. Haviland finest Limoges China. Decorated with pink flowers and sage green leaves with scroll work in gray; clouded burnished gold handles.

102 pieces, complete . $25 00

No. 4849. Haviland finest Limoges China. Flower decoration in the bright colors of purple, blue and delicate green, with sage green leaves artistically scattered over each piece.

102 pieces, complete . $25 00

No. 4848

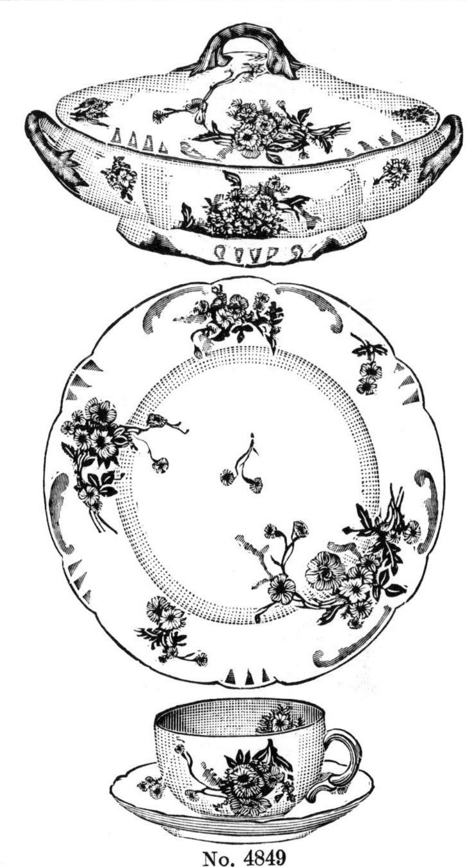

No. 4849

DINNER WARE—Continued

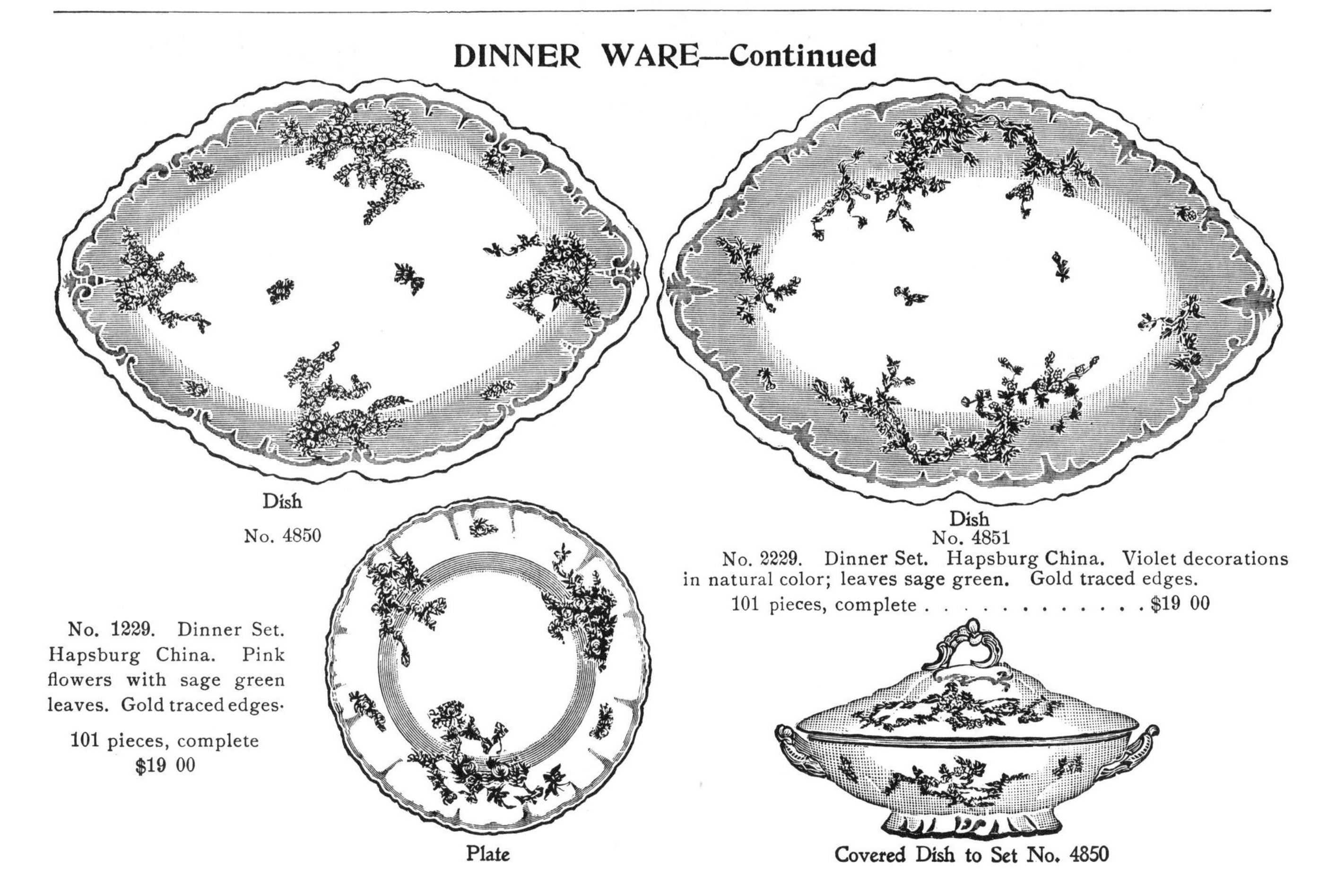

Dish

No. 4850

Dish

No. 4851

No. 2229. Dinner Set. Hapsburg China. Violet decorations in natural color; leaves sage green. Gold traced edges.

101 pieces, complete $19 00

No. 1229. Dinner Set. Hapsburg China. Pink flowers with sage green leaves. Gold traced edges.

101 pieces, complete $19 00

Plate

Covered Dish to Set No. 4850

DINNER WARE—Continued

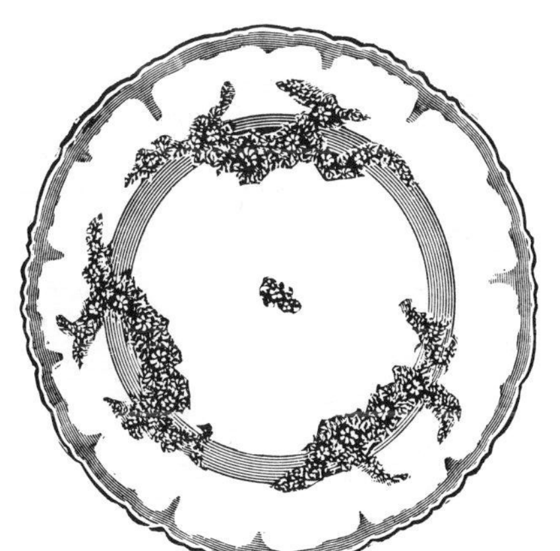

Plate to Set No. 4852

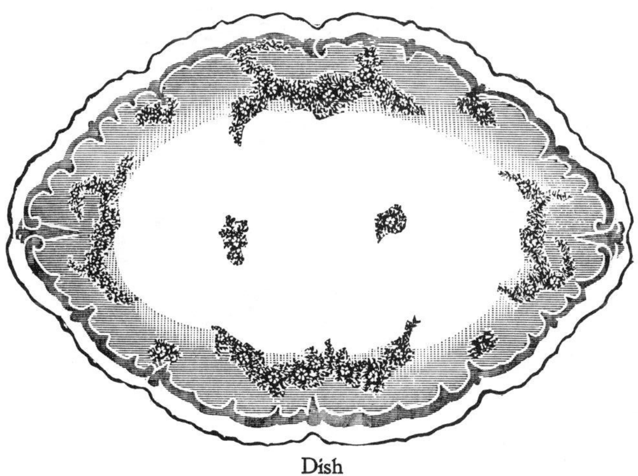

Dish
No. 4852

No. 4529—Dinner Set. Hapsburg China. Pink flowers, with vines and leaves in sage green; gold traced edges.
101 pieces, complete $19 00

Plate to Set No. 4851

Covered Dish to Set No. 4852

Covered Dish to Set No. 4851

DINNER WARE—Continued

For Actual Colors see Colored Insert B, following page 88

Covered Dish

Sauce Tureen

No. 4853

Plate

No. 824–A—"**Majestic**"

Maddock English Porcelain. Border decoration in flower and scroll work in combined tints of India red, cobalt blue, sage green and yellow; gold traced and gold outlined throughout. Can be purchased in any quantity desired, and matched at any time. Prices of single pieces mailed on application. Estimates furnished.

127 pieces, complete	$54 00
100 " "	44 00
56-piece Tea Set	16 00
Soup Set	11 40
Salad Set	5 80

Cup and Saucer

DINNER WARE—Continued

For Actual Colors see Colored Insert F, following page 154

Covered Dish

Sauce Tureen

Dish
No. 4854

Plate

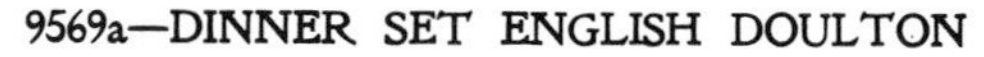

9569a—DINNER SET ENGLISH DOULTON

Border flower decoration in pink, blue and yellow flowers, with combined tints of sage green and light green scroll work. Handles, traced gold. Can be had in any quantity desired. Pieces matched at any time. Prices of single pieces mailed on application. Estimates furnished.

127 pieces, complete	$46 50
100 " "	37 90
56-piece Tea Set	12 65
Soup Set	9 00
Salad Set	5 50

Cup and Saucer

DINNER WARE—Continued

For Actual Colors see Colored Insert A, following page 78

Covered Dish

Sauce Tureen

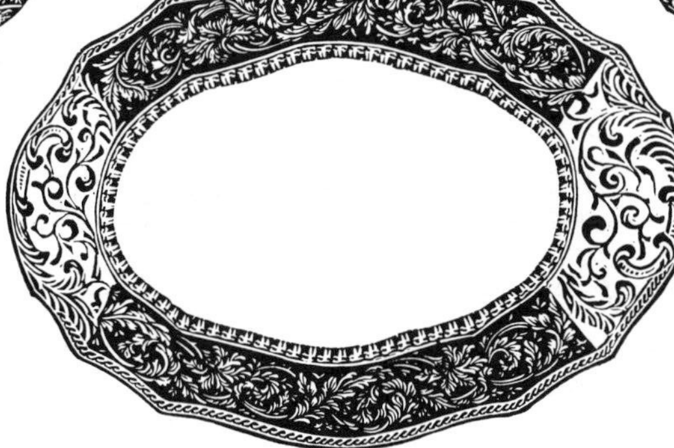

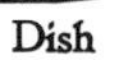

Dish

No. 4855

ENGLISH SEMI-PORCELAIN "GREEN BUNBURY"

Green border decoration, illuminated throughout with gold; gold traced edges and handles. Can be bought in any quantity desired, and matched at any time. Prices of single pieces mailed on application. Estimates furnished.

127 pieces, complete	$26 80
100 " "	22 00
55-piece Tea Set (no Bowl)	8 00
Soup Set	5 35
Salad Set	3 40

Plate

Cup and Saucer

DINNER WARE

(Continued)

For Actual Colors see Colored Insert G, following page 164

Covered Dish

Sauce Tureen

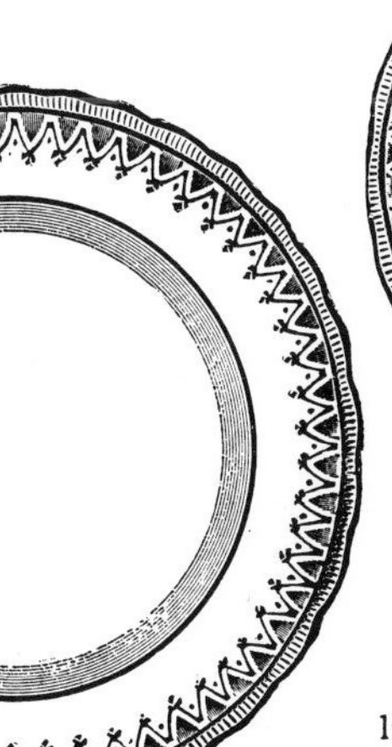

Plate

Dish. No. 4856

8279. FURNIVAL'S ENGLISH PORCELAIN

Green lace border, gold edge, gold traced handles, gold line through green border.

Can be bought in any quantity desired, and matched at any time. Prices of single pieces mailed on application. Estimates furnished.

127 pieces, complete, $26 80 56-piece Tea Set, $8 00
100 " " 22 00 Soup Set 5 35
Salad Set $3 40

Cup and Saucer

DINNER WARE—Continued

Covered Dish

Dish

Sauce Tureen

No. 4857

Dresden Onion Pattern of rich dark blue underglaze on English "Cauldon" Ware.

Can be bought in any quantity desired, and matched at any time. Prices of single pieces mailed on application. Estimates furnished.

126 pieces, complete	$23 65
100 " "	19 95
56-piece Tea Set	6 00
Soup Set	5 35
Salad Set	2 85

Plate

Cup and Saucer

DINNER WARE—Continued

Covered Dish

Dish

Sauce Tureen

Plate

No. 4858

ENGLISH CAULDON, H. 0278

Blue Delft Decoration.

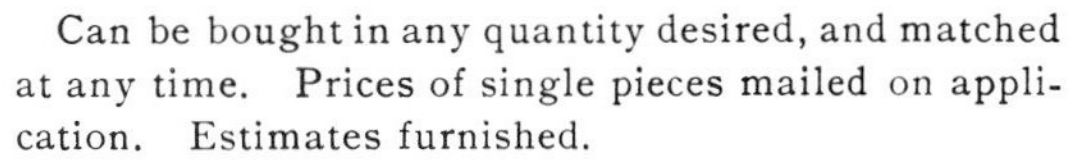

Can be bought in any quantity desired, and matched at any time. Prices of single pieces mailed on application. Estimates furnished.

127 pieces, complete	$23 65
100 " "	18 45
56-piece Tea Set	5 40
Soup Set	5 75
Salad Set	3 00

Cup and Saucer

DINNER WARE—Continued

Covered Dish

Dish

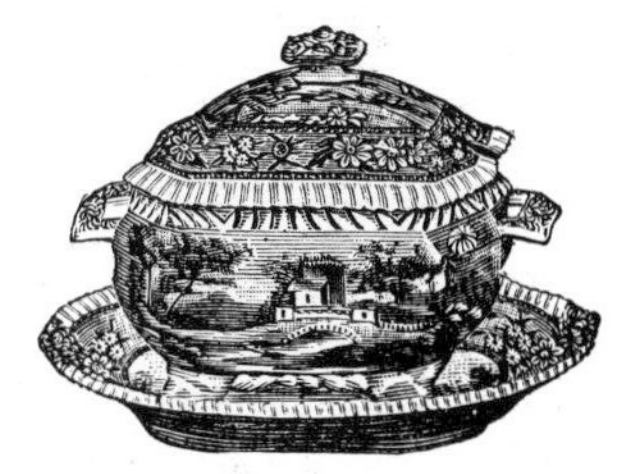

Sauce Tureen

No. 4859

COPELAND SPODE TOWER (ENGLISH)

Rich Dark Blue Decoration.

Can be bought in any quantity desired, and can be matched at any time. Estimates furnished on application.

126-piece Dinner Set	$28 75
100 pieces, complete	21 85
56-piece Tea Set	7 35
Soup Set	6 40
Salad Set	2 90

For Actual Colors see Colored Insert D, following page 122

Plate

Cup and Saucer

BRIC-A-BRAC AND A FEW LAMPS

DINNER WARE—Continued

For Actual Colors see Colored Insert B,
following page 88

Covered Dish

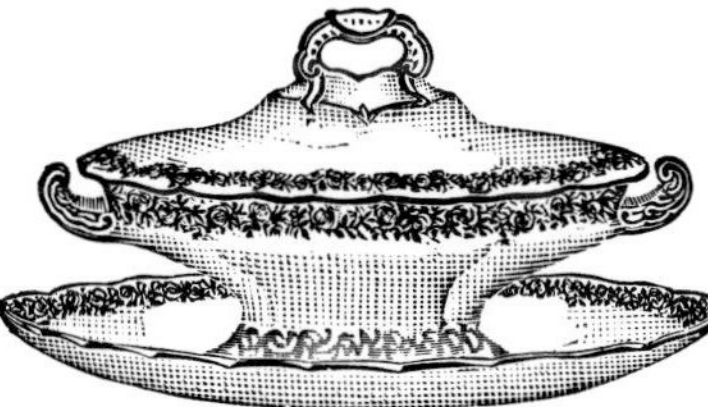

Sauce Tureen

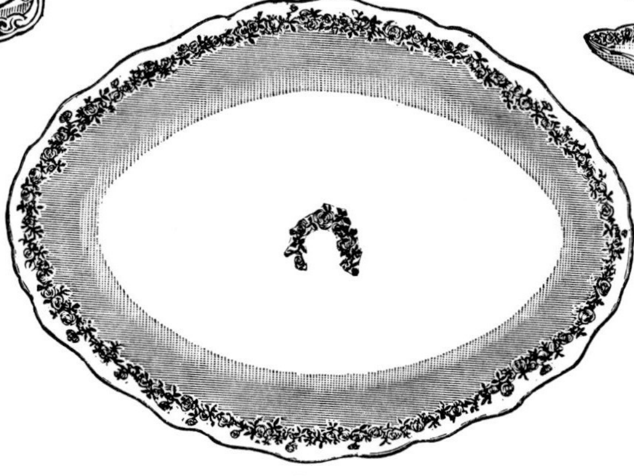

Dish

No. 4860

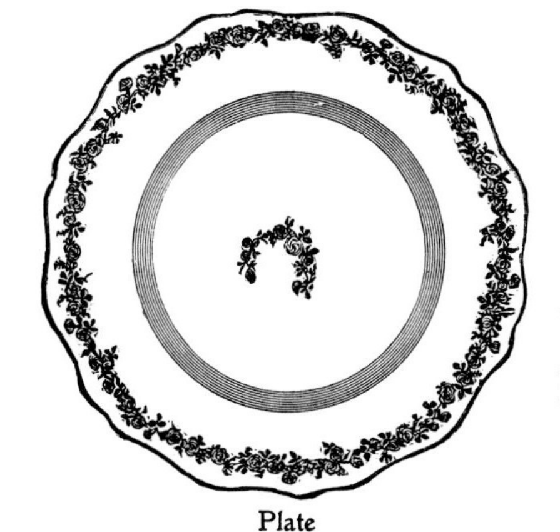

Plate

Cup and Saucer

No. 109. **Dinner Set. "Peerless"**

English porcelain ; border decoration in pink flowers with green leaves and sprays, handles traced gold.

Can be bought in any quantity desired, and matched at any time. Prices of single pieces mailed on application. Estimates furnished.

127 pieces, complete	$26 80
100 " "	22 00
Soup Set	5 35
Salad Set	3 40

DINNER WARE—Continued

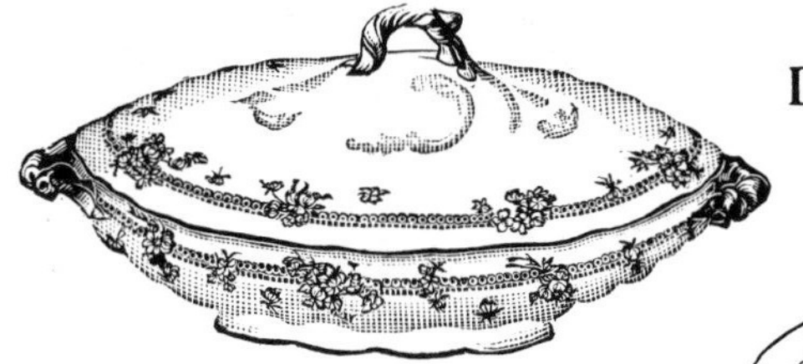

Covered Dish

Sauce Tureen

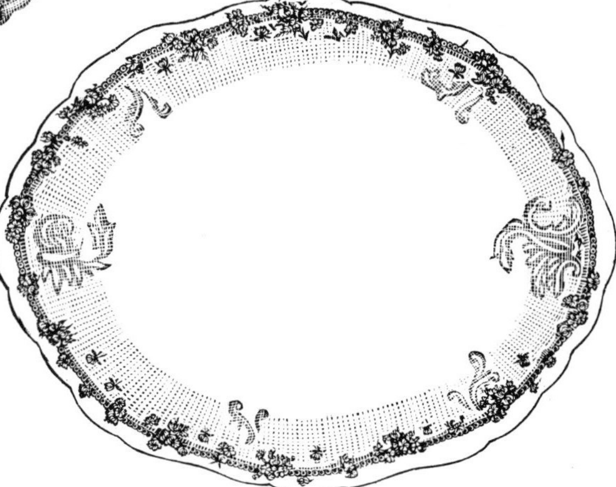

Dish

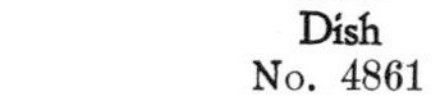

No. 4861

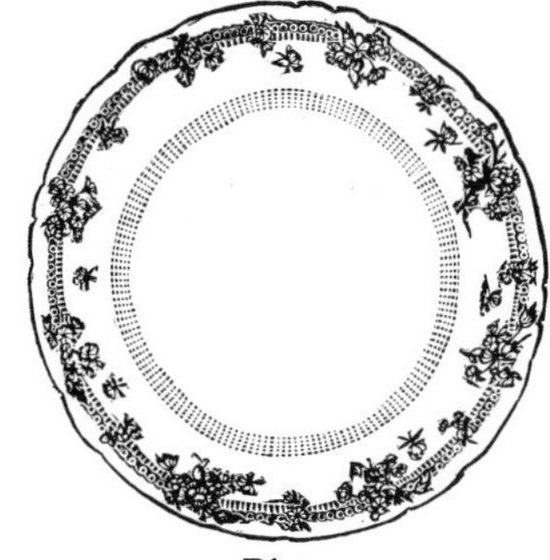

Plate

Cup and Saucer

COLUMBIA ELECTRIC GREEN ENGLISH PORCELAIN

Electric green border decoration of flowers and lace work. Can be bought in any quantity desired, and matched at any time. Estimates furnished.

127 pieces, complete	$22 70
100 pieces, complete	18 60
56-piece Tea Set	7 00
Soup Set	4 50
Salad Set	2 90

DINNER WARE—Continued

Covered Dish

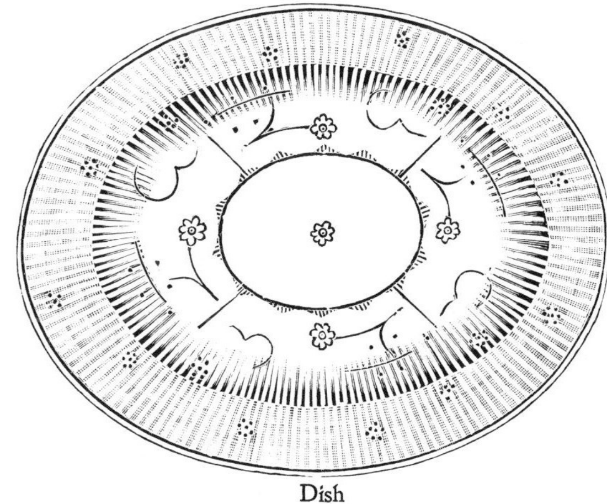

Dish

Sauce Tureen

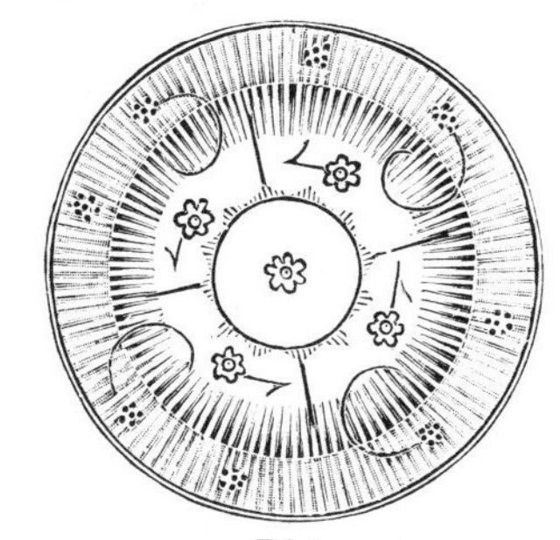

Plate

No. 4862

"COPENHAGEN"

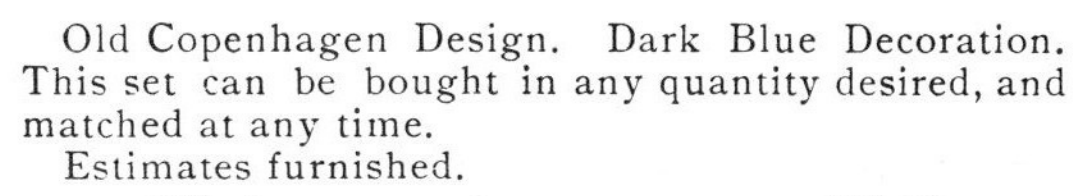

Old Copenhagen Design. Dark Blue Decoration. This set can be bought in any quantity desired, and matched at any time.

Estimates furnished.

127 pieces, complete	$21 00
100 " "	17 50
56-piece Tea Set	5 70
Soup Set	4 20
Salad Set	2 50

Cup and Saucer

For Actual Colors see Colored Insert D, following page 122

COMPOSITION OF

DINNER, TEA, ROAST, FISH, GAME, SOUP AND SALAD SETS

127-PIECE DINNER SET

12 Dinner Plates
12 Soup Plates
12 Breakfast Plates
12 Tea Plates
12 Preserve Saucers
12 Individual Butters
1 10-inch Dish
1 12-inch Dish
1 14-inch Dish
1 16-inch Dish
1 Baker
1 Covered Dish
2 Covered Dishes, round
1 Soup Tureen
1 Sauce Tureen and Stand
2 Pickles
1 Salad
12 Tea Cups and Saucers
6 Coffee Cups and Saucers

56-PIECE TEA SET

12 Plates Tea
12 Preserve Saucers
14 Tea Cups and Saucers
1 Tea Pot
1 Sugar Bowl
1 Creamer
1 Bowl
2 Cake Plates

34-PIECE ROAST SET

12 Plates (8½ inch)
12 Vegetable Saucers
1 16-inch Dish
2 Bakers
2 Covered Vegetable Dishes (4 pieces)
1 Sauce Tureen (3 pieces)

15-PIECE FISH SET

12 Plates
1 Dish
1 Sauce Tureen (2 pieces)

13-PIECE GAME SET

12 Plates
1 Platter

14-PIECE SOUP SET

12 Soup Plates
1 Soup Tureen (2 pieces)

13-PIECE SALAD SET

12 Salad Plates
1 Salad Bowl

COMPOSITION OF

DINNER, TEA, ROAST, FISH, GAME, SOUP and SALAD SETS, TOILET SETS, BREAKFAST SETS, Etc.—Continued

100-PIECE DINNER SET

12 Dinner Plates
12 Breakfast Plates
12 Soup Plates
12 Fruit Saucers
12 Individual Butters
1 10-inch Dish
1 12-inch Dish
1 16-inch Dish
1 Salad
1 Soup Tureen
1 Sauce Tureen and Stand
2 Covered Vegetable Dishes
2 Uncovered Vegetable Dishes
2 Pickles
12 Tea Cups and Saucers

13-PIECE CHOP SET

12 Plates, 7½-inch
1 Chop Platter

55-PIECE BREAKFAST SET

12 Plates, 7½-inch
12 Breakfast Coffee Cups and Saucers
1 10-inch Dish
1 Baker
12 Individual Butters
1 12-inch Dish
1 Covered Dish
2 Bread Plates

11-PIECE TOILET SET

Same pieces as in the 12-piece set with the soap dish counting only two pieces, as the drainer is attached.

70-PIECE LUNCH SET

12 Plates, 7½ inch
12 Individual Butters
1 12-inch Dish
1 14-inch Dish
2 Bakers
2 Bread Plates
12 Saucers
12 Tea Cups aud Saucers
2 Casseroles

12-PIECE TOILET SET

1 Large Water Pitcher
1 Basin
1 Slop Jar (2 pieces)
1 Chamber (2 pieces)
1 Small Water Pitcher
1 Brush Vase
1 Mug
1 Soap Dish (3 pieces)

TOILET WARE

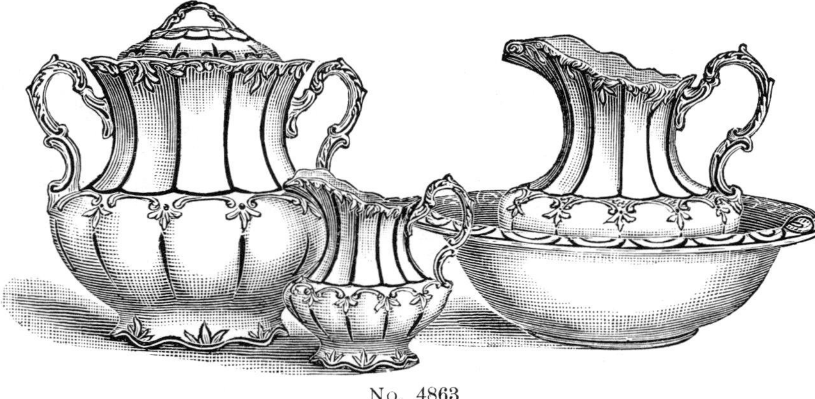

No. 4863

No. 376—**Toilet Set. "Savoy." Olive**

Shaded olive on top and bottom with cream color in center. Panels, edges and handles traced in gold.

12 pieces, complete $16 50

No. 4864

No. 676—**Toilet Set. "Girard"**

Delicate green background with Fuchsia decoration in darker green. Gold tracings, edges and handles.

12 pieces, complete $15 00

TOILET WARE—Continued

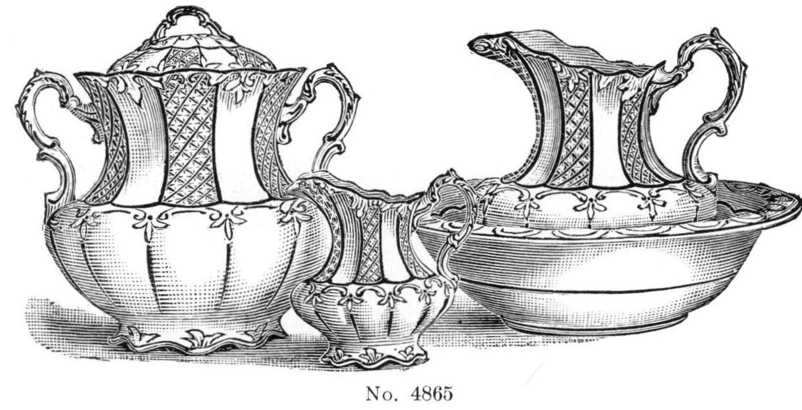

No. 4865

Toilet Set. "Savoy" Gold Lattice

Panels, edges and handles gold traced, with alternate panels of gold lattice work.

12 pieces, complete $13 15

No. 4866

No. 975—**Toilet Set. "Leroy"**

Wild rose decoration in pink and white flowers. Edgès and neck in delicate pink. Gold edges and gold traced handles.

12 pieces, complete $11 25

TOILET WARE—Continued

No. 4867

For Actual Colors see Colored Insert E, following page 132

No. 8641 C—**Toilet Set. "Girard"**

Field rose decoration in either tints of yellow or pink, with leaves to harmonize. Embossing, edges and handles gold traced.

12 pieces, complete $10 50

No. 4868

For Actual Colors see Colored Insert E, following page 132

No. 2741 C—**Toilet Set. "Girard"**

Pansy decoration in the natural color of the flower, with green leaves. Gold traced edges and handles,

12 pieces, complete $10 50

TOILET WARE—Continued

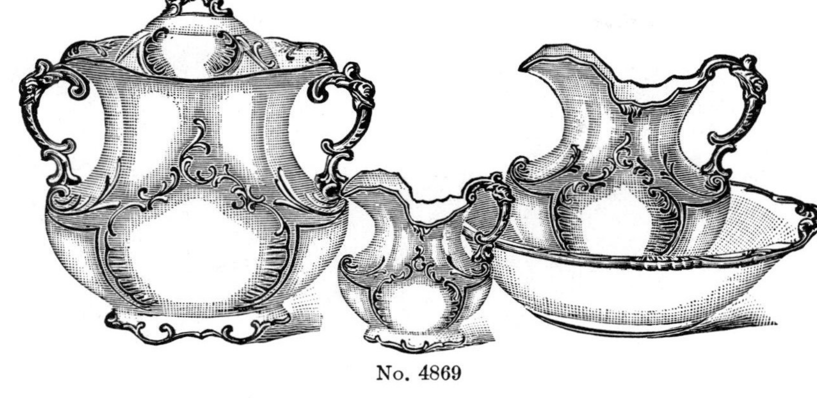

No. 4869

Toilet Set. "Torquay"

Shaded decorations in either yellow, rose pink or dark green or blue. Handles and embossed parts being traced with gold.

12 pieces, complete $9 75

No. 4870

No. 0621. **Toilet Set. "Hecla"**

Shaded tints in either pink, blue or yellow. Embossed parts, edges and handles gold traced.

12 pieces, complete $8 25

For Actual Colors see Colored Insert E, following page 132

TOILET WARE—Continued

No. 4871

Toilet Set. "Empress"

Solid colors in either purple, sage green or dark blue.

11 pieces, complete $7 50

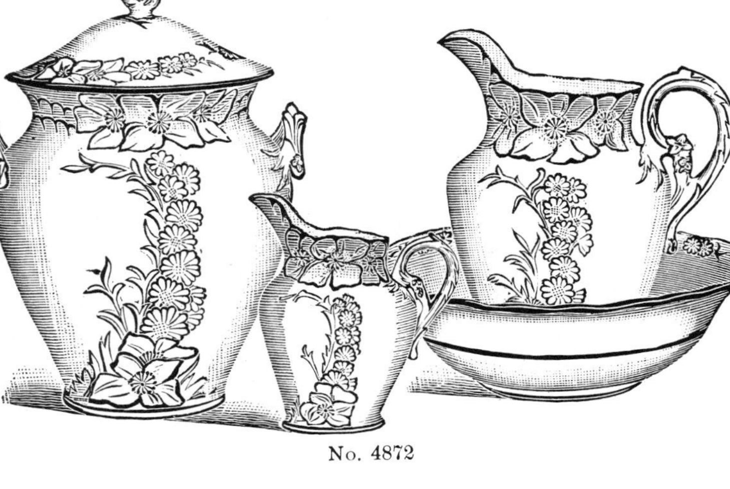

No. 4872

Toilet Set. No. 0210 D

White, with embossed flowers traced throughout with gold.

12 pieces, complete $7 50

TOILET WARE—Continued

No. 4873

For Actual Colors see Colored Insert E, following page 132

No. 6321—**Toilet Set. "Hecla"**

Edges, neck and panels in either green, blue or maroon, with flower decoration in panel effect. Gold traced handles and edges.

12 pieces, complete $7 35

No. 4874

No. 9221 **Toilet Set. "Hecla"**

Iris decoration in violet, with leaves in delicate green, edges clouded gold.

12 pieces, complete. $6 00

For Actual Colors see Colored Insert E, following page 132

TOILET WARE—Continued

No. 4875

No. 1221—Toilet Set. "Hecla"

Wild rose and morning glory decoration in either pink, blue or green, gold tracing on embossed parts and edge.

12 pieces, complete $5 25

No. 4876

No. 9151 C—Toilet Set. "Astor"

Decoration of rambling roses in either pink roses, tea roses or red roses, with natural green leaves ; embossed parts in gold, traced gold edges.

12 pieces, complete **$12 50**

TOILET WARE—Continued

No. 4877

Toilet Set. "Hero"

Delft decoration in either dark blue or light green.

11 pieces, complete $4 00

No. 4878

Toilet Set "Hero"

Small flower decoration in plain colors, pink or blue.

11 pieces, complete $3 45

For Actual Colors see Colored Insert E, following page 132

FISH SETS

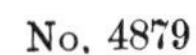
No. 4879

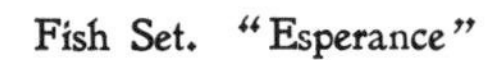
Fish Set. "Esperance"

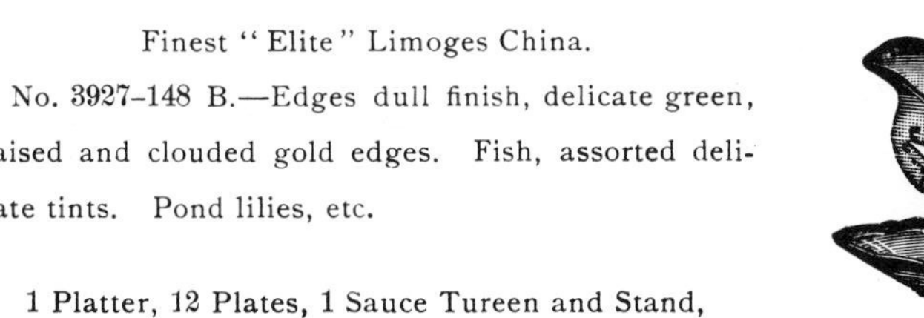
Finest "Elite" Limoges China.

No. 3927–148 B.—Edges dull finish, delicate green, raised and clouded gold edges. Fish, assorted delicate tints. Pond lilies, etc.

1 Platter, 12 Plates, 1 Sauce Tureen and Stand,
15 pieces, complete, $38 00

FISH SETS—Continued

No. 4880

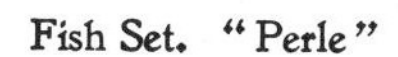

Fish Set. "Perle"

No. 4248–1881. Finest "Elite" Limoges China. Dark blue border, showing fish net in gold, with center decoration of fish and water; clouded gold edges.

14 pieces, complete . . . $35 00

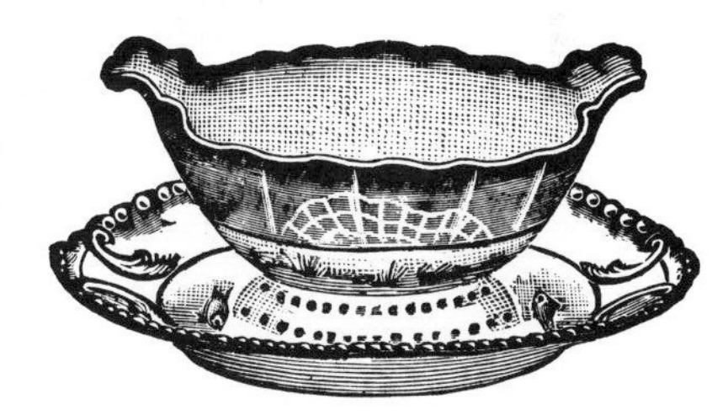

FISH SETS—Continued

No. 4881

Fish Set. "Mireille"

Finest "Elite" Limoges China

No. 8997–9031.—Center decoration of fish with border of small fish and gold lace; gold edge and clouded gold handles,

15 pieces, complete $31 75

FISH SETS—Continued

No. 4882

Fish Set. "Perle"

No. 0448-2091. Finest "Elite" Limoges China. Maroon or light blue border, with gold lace. Center decoration showing fish in water. Edges burnished gold.

14 pieces, complete $27 50

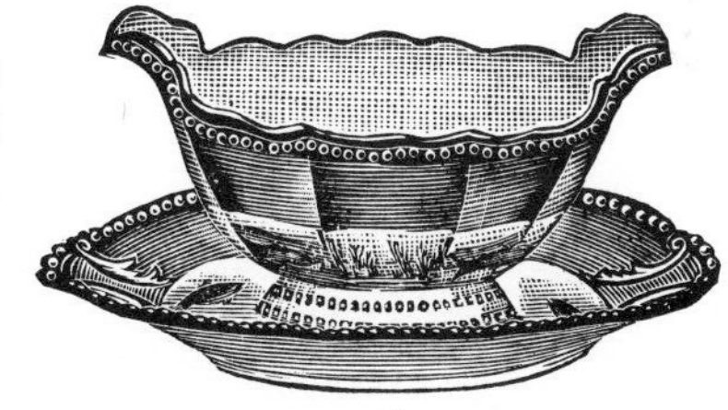

FISH SETS—Continued

No. 4883.

Fish Set. "Duchess"

Finest "Elite" Limoges China.

No. 3237-5121.—Delicate tinted background in light blue, fish in assorted delicate tints; edges clouded, and traced gold on embossed edges.

1 Dish, 12 Plates, 1 Sauce Tureen and Stand.

15 pieces, complete $23 00

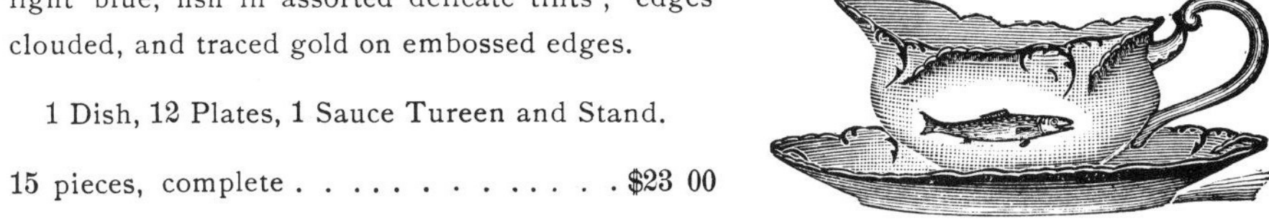

FISH SETS—Continued

No. 4884

Fish Set. "Perle"

No. 5048–6181.—"Elite" Limoges China, green border, with center decoration of water showing small fish in natural colors, with weeds, etc., and flower border on shoulder of plates and platter; edges best burnished gold.

14 pieces, complete 22 50

GAME SETS

No. 4885

Game Set

No. 8234–9471. "Elite" Limoges China. Border in either maroon or green, game centers, with gold edge and gold lace on shoulder of plate.

15 pieces, complete $25 00

GAME SETS—Continued

No. 4886

No. 3548–2491—**Elite Limoges China**

Shaded green border with flowers and game centers, clouded gold edges.

15 pieces, complete **$19 50**

CHOP SETS

For Actual Colors see Colored Insert G, following page 164

No. 4887

No. 197-84—Chop Set. "Turgot"

Finest Elite Limoges China, cream body, border with delicate green tint, burnished gold edge; gold star center.

12 Plates and 1 Chop Dish . . . $20 25

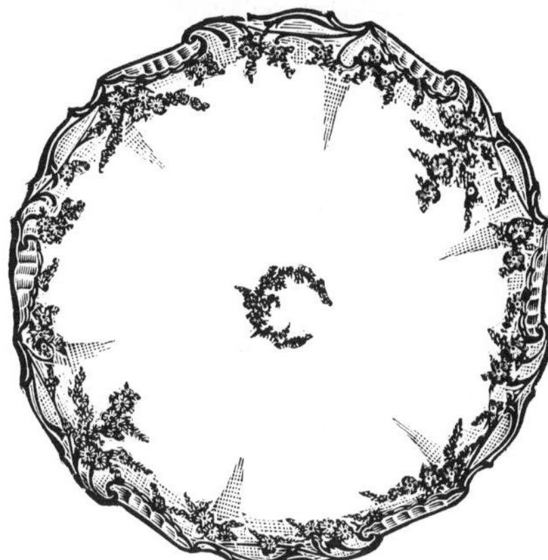

No. 4888

No. 3121—Chop Set. "Esperance"

Finest Elite Limoges China, with border and center decoration of delicate green flowers and burnished gold leaves, the flowers also being outlined with gold, fancy traced burnished gold edges.

12 Plates and 1 Chop Dish . . $14 85

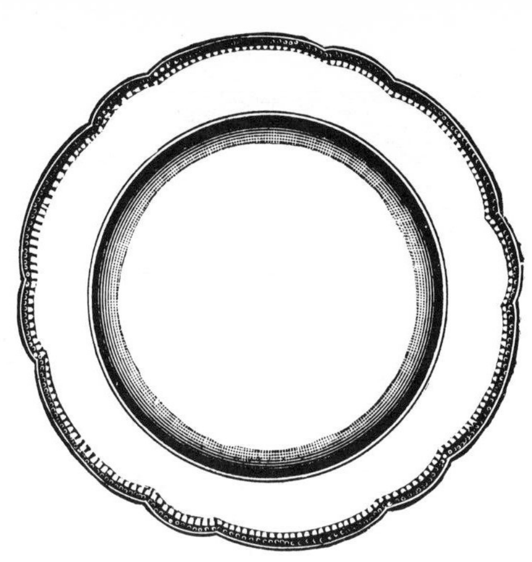

For Actual Colors see Colored Insert A, following Page 78

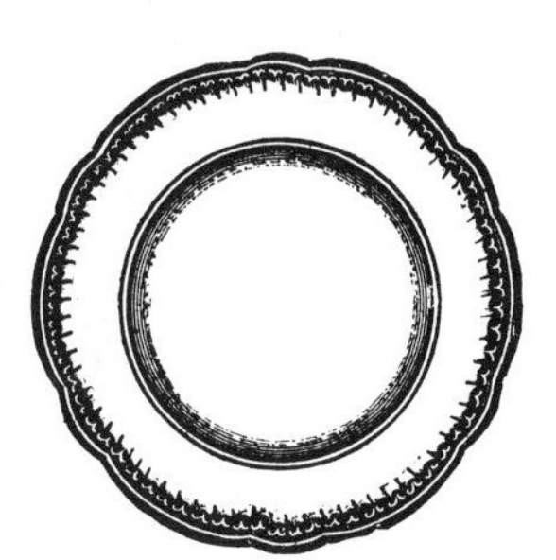

No. 4889

No. 7843—Chop Set. "Napoleon"

Finest Limoges China, burnished gold lace work border.

12 Plates, 1 Chop Dish $8 00

(Chop Sets can also be obtained from many of our Dinner Ware patterns.)

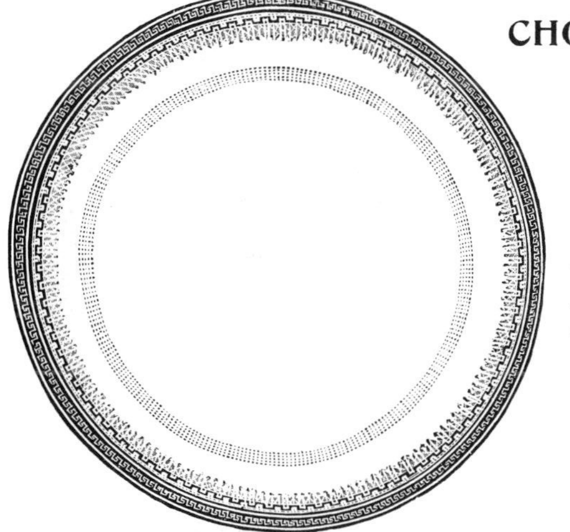

CHOP SETS—Continued

No. 4890

No. 3178 H—**Chop Set. "Cauldon"**

Three lines of scoured gold on edge, with key decoration on center band in black, and hair brown border extending toward center of plate.

12 Plates and 1 Chop Dish . . $24 40

For Actual Colors see Colored Insert C, following page 100

No. 4891

No. 2682—**Chop Set. St. Germain**

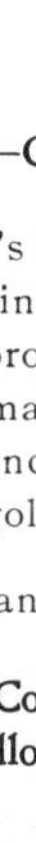

Haviland's Limoges China. Border decoration in delicate green flowers, with hair brown and lavender edge; border of small flowers on shoulder of plate and fancy rosette center; clouded burnished gold edges.

12 Plates and 1 Chop Dish . $10 55

For Actual Colors see Colored Insert D, following page 122

No. 4892

Chop Set. "Brown Arabesque"

No. 8765.—Finest Limoges China. Border decoration in hair brown with gold edge.
12 Plates and 1 Chop Dish................$6 65

For Actual Colors see Colored Insert G, following page 164

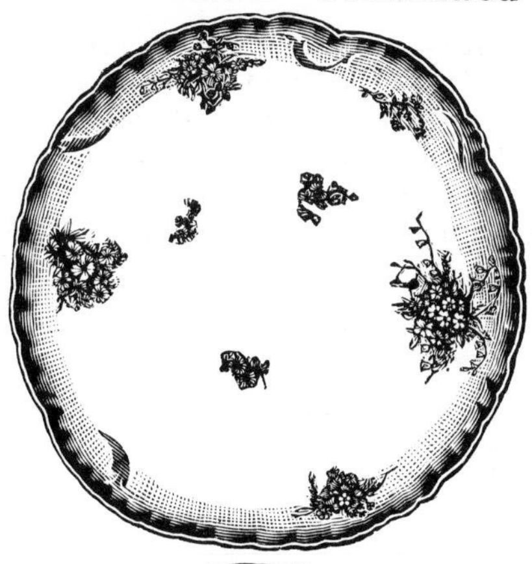

No. 4893

No. 3692 A.—**Chop Set. "Rouen"**

Haviland's Finest Limoges China, decorated with trailing arbutus in delicate pink, with background of maidenhair fern in light green, small sprays being scattered artistically over each article.
12 Plates and 1 Chop Dish $5 10

For Actual Colors see Colored Insert F, following page 154

No. 4894

Chop Set. "Green Bunbury"

English Semi-Porcelain

Green border decoration illuminated throughout with gold, gold traced edges.
12 Plates and 1 Chop Dish $3 00

For Actual Colors see Colored Insert A, following page 78

CHOP SET—SALAD SET

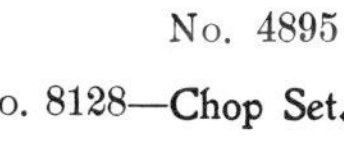

No. 4895

No. 8128—**Chop Set. "Perle"**

Elite Limoges China

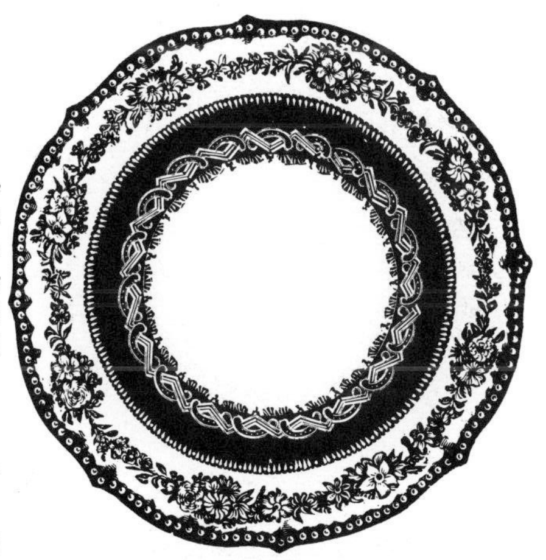

Border decoration of flowers in bouquets; connecting sprigs of flowers in pink, purple and yellow, sage green leaves; band below shoulder in either maroon or dark green. Burnished gold edge and gold lace on colored band. Chop dish, 12 inches across.

13 pieces, complete $21 65

Plates can also be had in this pattern, as follows:

Dinner Plate,	8½ in.	per doz.,	$18 75
Soup "	8 in.	"	17 50
Breakfast "	7½ in.	"	16 20
Tea "	6½ in.	"	13 50
Band B "	5½ in.	"	10 00

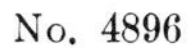

No. 4896

No. 2577—**Salad Set. "Souvenir"**

Finest Limoges china, decorated with violets in the natural color; edges ivory and burnished gold.

Salad bowl, 11x9, 4½ inches deep. 12 plates and salad bowl, complete $16 55

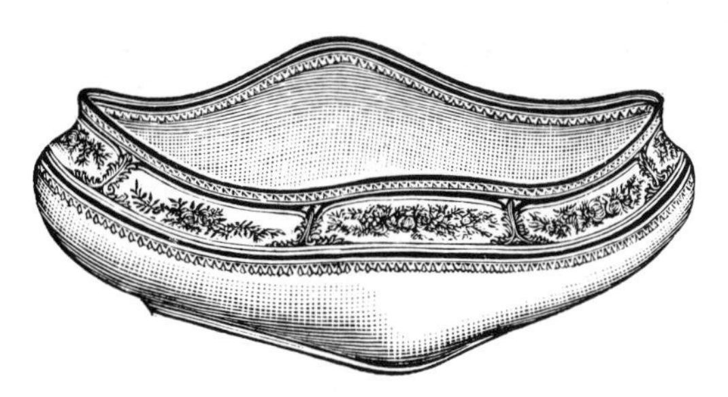

No. 4897

No. 2912—**Berry Set. "Indus"**

English Wedgwood china, border decoration of panels of flowers in pink and blue, gold leaves and gold decoration throughout.

13 pieces, complete . . . $28 40

For Actual Colors see Colored Insert F, following page 154

No. 4898

No. 2674—**Berry Set. "Brighton"**

English Wedgwood china, underglazed dark blue border decoration and gold lace.

13 pieces, complete . . . $14 95

For Actual Colors see Colored Insert D, following page 122

No. 4899

No. 9416—**Berry Set. "Perle"**

Elite Limoges china, rococo border decoration in sage green and light green with clusters of flowers in pink; fancy center, edges burnished gold.

13 pieces, complete . . . $6 55

For Actual Colors see Colored Insert B, following page 88

BERRY SETS—Continued

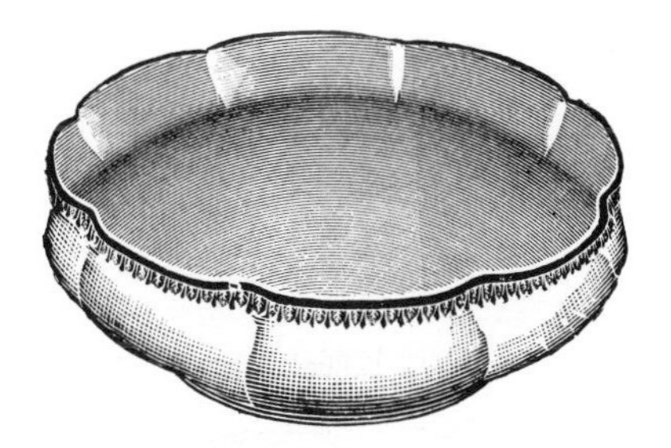

No. 4900

No. 7843—**Berry Set.** **"Napoleon"**

Finest Limoges China. Gold lace work border; gold edge.

13 pieces, complete $5 65

For Actual Colors see Colored Insert A, following page 78

No. 4901

No. 824A—**Berry Set**

Maddock English porcelain. Bright red flowers with blue rococo, fancy center, gold traced.

13 pieces, complete $4 80

For Actual Colors see Colored Insert B, following page 88

No. 4902

No. 0603—**Berry Set.** **"Perle"**

Finest "Elite" Limoges China. Border decoration in delicate pink and yellow flowers, green leaves, connecting vines in blue, gold edge.

13 pieces. complete $4 35

For Actual Colors see Colored Insert F, following page 153

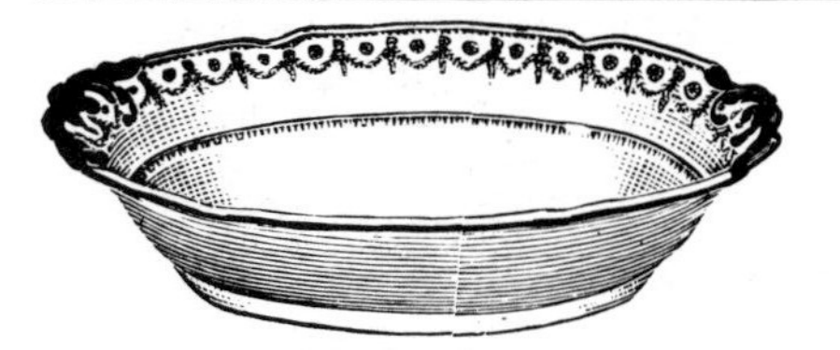

BERRY SETS—Continued

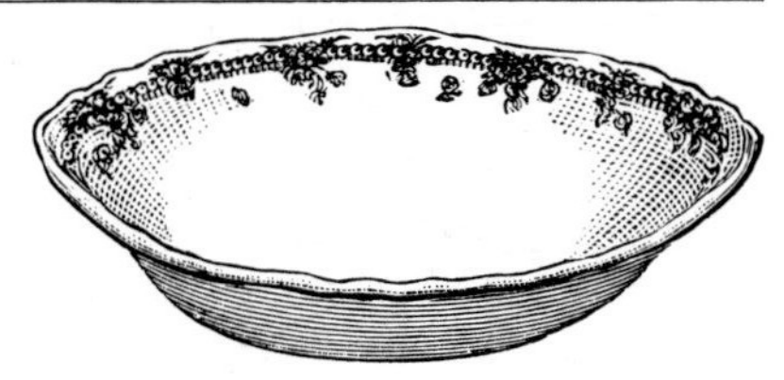

No. 4903

4904

No. 4905

No. 4906

No. 7159—**Berry Set. "Napoleon"**

Festoon, green border decoration, green lace on edge.

13 pieces, complete . $3 60.

For Actual Colors see Colored Insert D, following page 122

No. 6714—**Berry Set "Vincennes"**

Haviland's Limoges China. Morning-glory decoration in pink and blue flowers, green leaves.

13 pieces, complete. . $2 80

For Actual Colors see Colored Insert C, following page 100

No. 289-615—**Berry Set**

Vienna China. Border decoration of light blue flowers and green leaves, gold traced edge.

13 pieces, complete . $2 00

For Actual Colors see Colored Insert F, following page 154

Berry Set

Columbia electric green. Border decoration in light blue or Celeste.

13 pieces, complete . $1 05

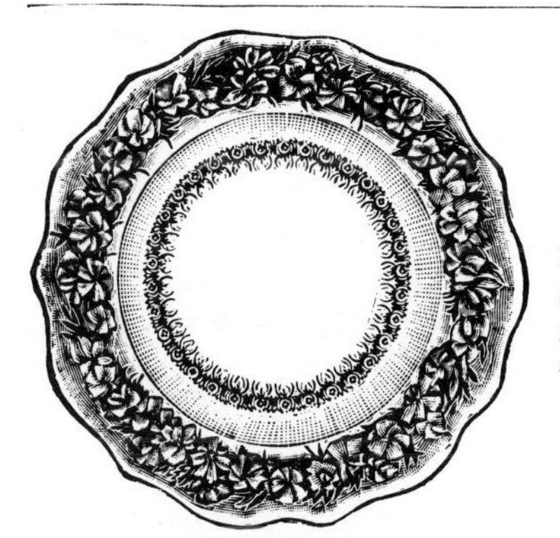

LIMOGES CHINA. No. 3087

Border pattern with background of light blue, and carnation decoration in pink, yellow and green leaves. Fancy gold lace and clouded gold handles. A cream colored background extends a short distance from the edge of each article below the carnation border.

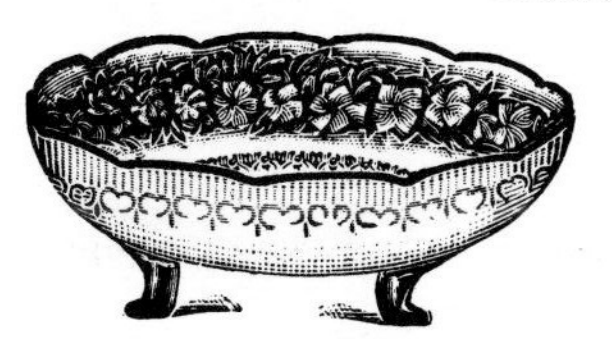

No. 4909

Fruit or Berry Dish, on Feet

7 inch. . . . . .each, $3 50
8 inch. . . . . . . " 4 10

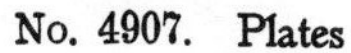

No. 4907. **Plates**

8½ inch or dinner size, per doz.	$14 00
7½ inch or entree size, "	12 30
6½ inch or dessert size, "	10 10
5½ inch or bread and butter size, "	8 00

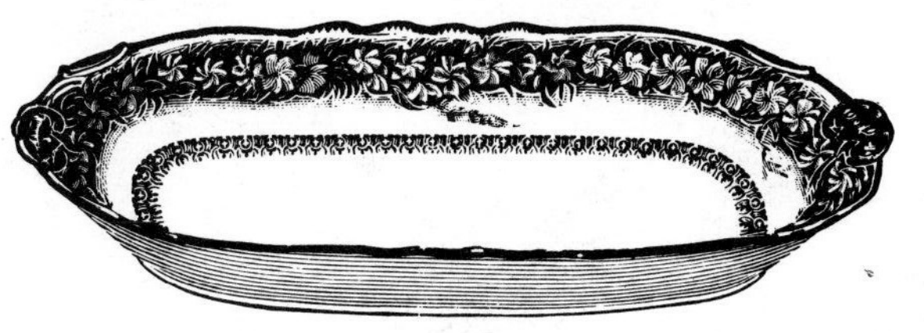

No. 4908

Ice Cream Tray

8½ x 16 inches . . . . each, $4 50

No. 4910. **Cracker Jar**

6¾ inches high . . . . . each, $4 00

No. 4911

Chocolate Jug

9 inches high, capacity about 7 cups . . each, $3 35

For actual Colors see Colored Insert B, following page 88

LIMOGES CHINA

No. 3087—Continued

No. 4912

Covered Muffin or Hot Cake Dish

9½ inches across plate . . each, $4 40

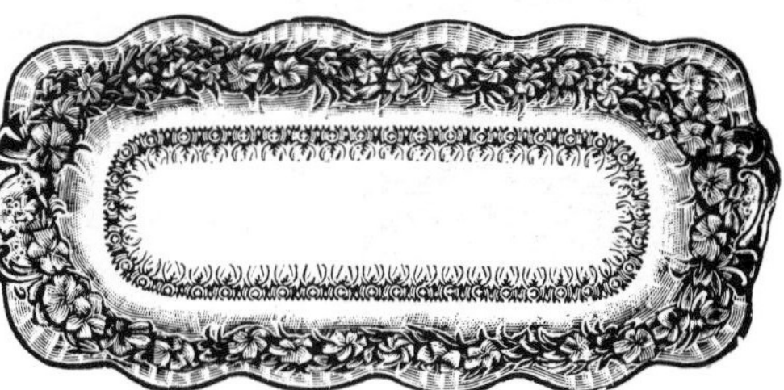

No. 4914

Celery Tray

5½ x 12 inches . . . . each, $2 30

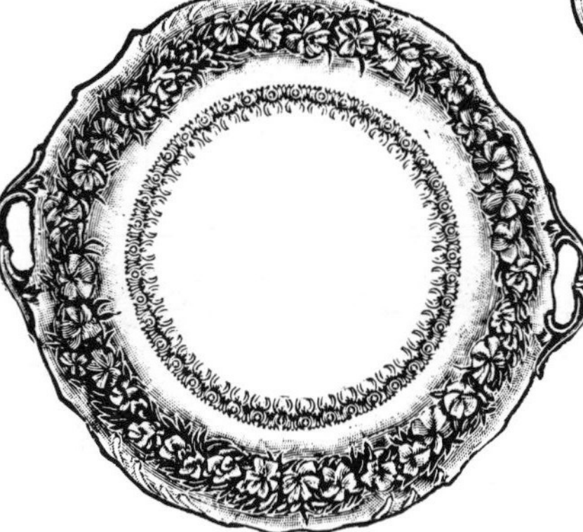

No. 4913

Cake Dish

Open Handles

10½ inches across . . . . . each, $2 15

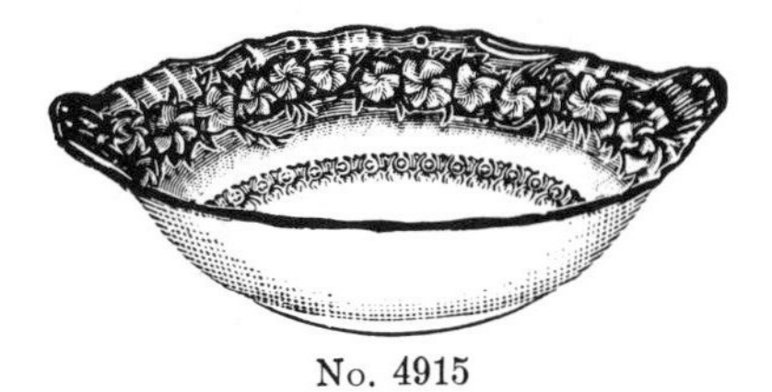

No. 4915

Salad or Fruit Bowl

With handles

11 inches across . . . . each, $3 10
9¼ inches across . . . . " 2 40

For Actual Colors see Colored Insert B, following page 88

No. 4916

Comport or Fruit Dish

Handle on side

10⅜ inches across . . . . each, $1 85

LIMOGES CHINA. No. 3087
(Continued)

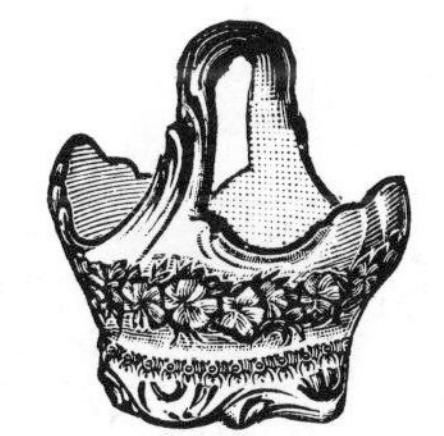

No. 4917

Handled Sugar Basket

5 x 4 inches . . . . each, $2 10

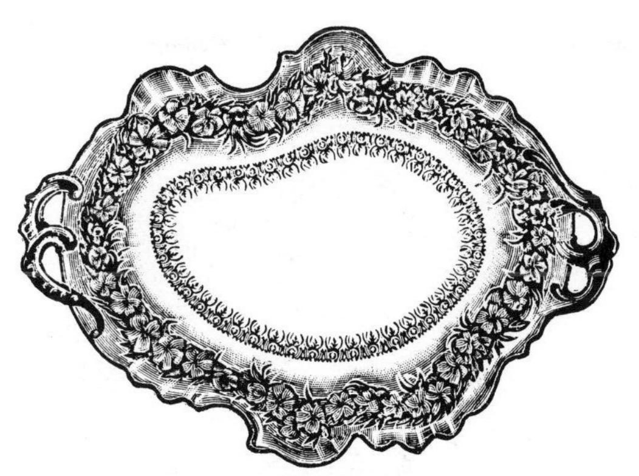

No. 4918

Fancy Tray

Open handles, 9 x 12½ inches

Each $2 70

No. 4919

Olive or Radish Dish

7¼ inches from handle to handle

Each $1 20

No. 4920

Handled Bon Bon or Olive Dish

7 x 7 inches . . . . each, $1 45

For Actual Colors see Colored Insert B, following page 88

No. 4921

Olive or Bon Bon Dish

4½ x 7¾ inches . . . . . each, $1 00

LIMOGES CHINA. No. 3087
(Continued)

No. 4922
Sugar
5½ inches high . . . . each, $1 95

No. 4923
Tea Pot
7 inches high . . . . each, $2 60

No. 4924
Creamer
5 inches high . . . . each, $1 25

No. 4925

No. 4926

No. 4927

Croton Set
Covered Soap Dish, Tooth Brush Mug, Handled Mug
3 pieces, complete $4 70

For Actual Colors see Colored Insert B, following page 88

LIMOGES CHINA. No. 3087—Continued

No. 4928
Hair Receiver
Opening in top, 2¼ inches high
Each $1 45

No. 4929
Bon Bon or Footed Comport
6½ inches across ; 3¼ inches high
Each $2 30

No. 4930
Tea Strainer
With stand
Each $1 55

No. 4931
Bouillon Cup and Saucer
Per dozen $15 90

No. 4932
Tea Cups and Saucers
Per dozen $14 00

No. 4933
Chocolate Cups and Saucers
Per dozen $12 95

No. 4934
After-Dinner Coffees
Per dozen $9 90

For Actual Colors see Colored Insert B, following page 88

LIMOGES ELITE CHINA. No. 5128

Border decoration of lilies of the valley in gray, with leaves of delicate green and background of buff; edges clouded burnished gold, handles stippled gold.

No. 4935
No. 383—**Chocolate Pot. "Perle"**
9½ inches high, each, $3 20

No. 4936
Ice Cream Tray. "Perle"
10½ x 16½
Each $3 20

No. 4938
No. 173—**Pudding Dish, with Plate. "Perle"**
Plate, 12 inches across. Dish, 9½ inches across
3 pieces, complete, with fireproof inner, $5 45

For Actual Colors see Colored Insert G, following page 100

No. 4937
No. 793—**Black Coffee Pot "Perle"**
9½ inches high, each, $3 25

No. 4939. **Plates**

Dinner size, 8½ inch . .	per dozen,	$10 00
Breakfast or entree size, 7½ in.	"	9 00
Tea or Dessert, size 6½-inch	"	6 75
Bread and Butter, 5½-inch	"	5 40

ELITE LIMOGES CHINA No. 5128—Continued

No. 4940

Salad or Fruit Bowl. "Perle" No. 663

10 inches across, each $1 75

No. 4943

Oat Meal, Berry or Ice Cream Saucers

Per dozen $4 60

No. 4944

Chocolate Cup and Saucer

Per dozen $10 50

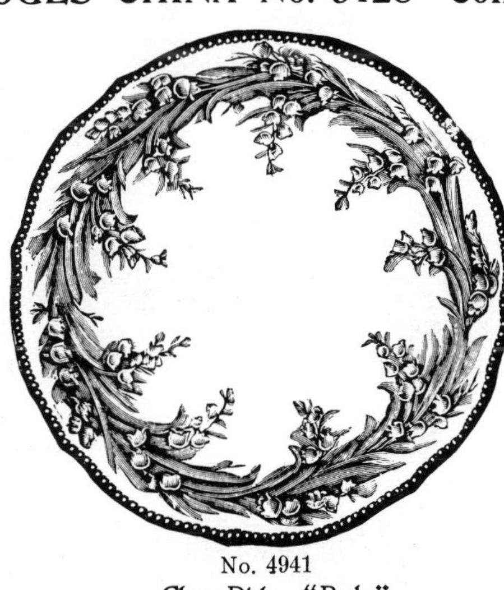

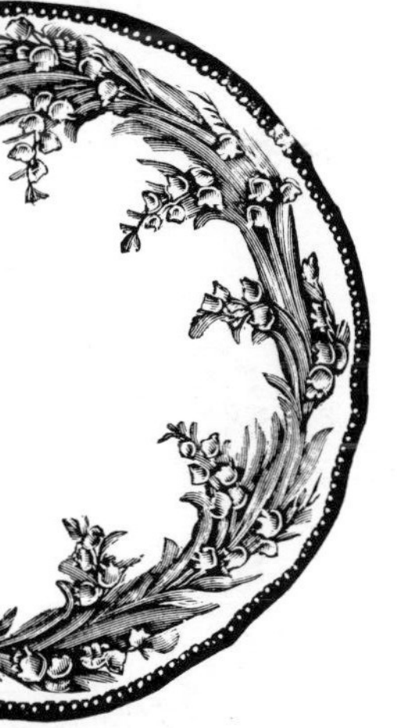

No. 4941

Chop Dish. "Perle"

12 inches across, each $2 45

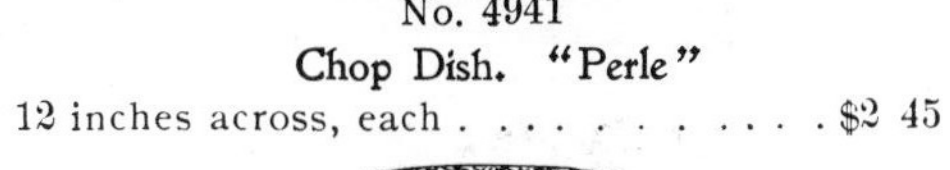

No. 4945

Tea Cups, per dozen	$10 50
A. D. Cups, "	8 55

For Actual Colors see Colored Insert C, following page 100

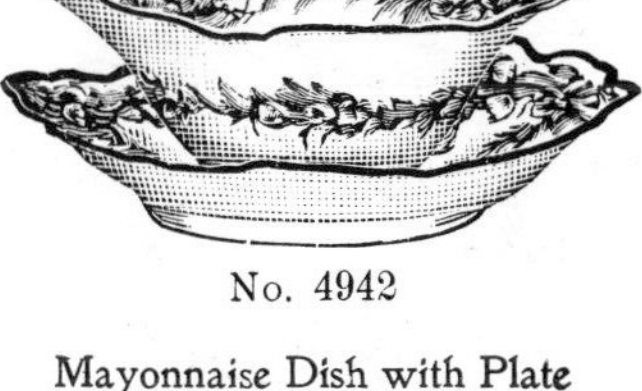

No. 4942

Mayonnaise Dish with Plate

No. 893

Plate 6½ x 5½,	2 pieces, complete
Dish 5¾ x 4½,	$1 50

No. 4946

Bouillon Cup and Saucer

Per dozen $12 45

ELITE LIMOGES CHINA
(Continued)

No. 4947
Cake Plate
10½ inches across from outside to outside of handle, each $1 70

No. 4948
Hair Receiver. "Perle"
4½ inches across, opening in top, each . $1 70

No. 4949
Olive or Bon Bon. No. 473
5 x 7½ inches, each $0 50

No. 4950
Fancy Tray. "Perle." No. 783
7½ x 12 . . . . $1 70 each

No. 4951
Sugar and Creamer. "Argent" No. 283
Sugar, 6½ in. high. Creamer, 5¼ in. high
Two pieces $2 55

No, 4952
Tea Pot. "Argent"
8 inches high, each $2 30

For Actual Colors see Colored Insert C, following page 100

FINEST "ELITE" LIMOGES CHINA—No. 9416

Border decoration with green daisies, small rosebuds and rococo design in sage green. Clouded burnished gold edges ; fancy center of rococo design and small rosebuds.

No. 4953
Olive, Pickle or Bon Bon
4¾x7½ . . . . . . each, $0 45

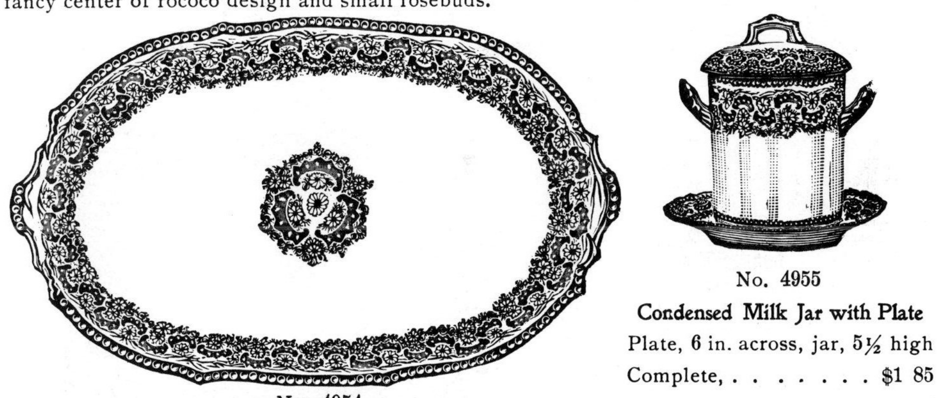

No. 4955
Condensed Milk Jar with Plate
Plate, 6 in. across, jar, 5½ high
Complete, ... $1 85

No. 4954

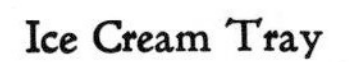

Ice Cream Tray
10 x 16 inches . . . . each, $3 15

No. 4856
Pudding Dish and Plate
Plate, 12 inches across ; pudding dish, 9-inch opening. 3 pieces, with fireproof inner.
Per set $5 60

For Actual Colors see Colored Insert B, following page 88

No, 4957
Celery Tray
5½ x 12½ inches . . . each, $1 50

ELITE LIMOGES CHINA. No. 9416—Continued

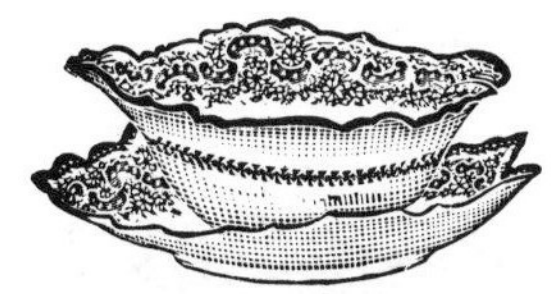

No. 4958

Mayonnaise Dish with Tray

2 pieces $1 75

No. 4961

Chocolate Jug

9 inches high ; capacity about 9 or 10 cups . . . . each, $3 35

No. 4959

Brush and Comb Tray

8 x 12 inches . . . . each, $1 60

For Actual Colors see Colored Insert B, following page 88

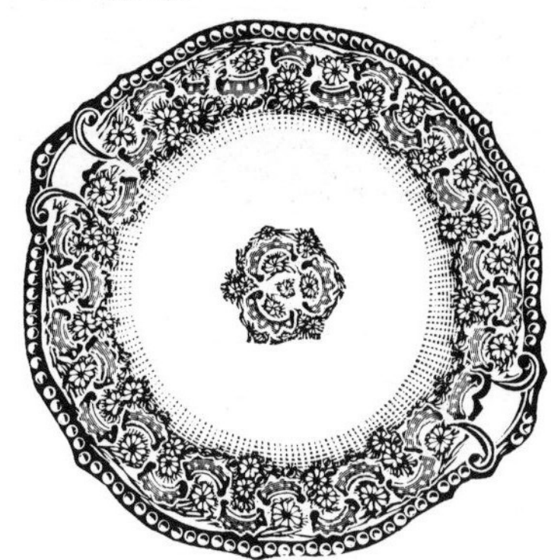

No. 4960

Cake Plate

Open handles ; 10¼ inches from edge to edge . . . . each, $1 60

No. 4962

Tea Pot

6 inches high . . . . each, $2 10

ELITE LIMOGES CHINA. No. 9416—Continued

No. 4963

Hair Receiver

Hole in top to receive hair; 2½ inches high

Each. $1 15

No. 4964

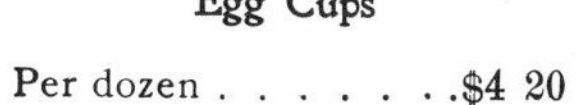

Egg Cups

Per dozen $4 20

No. 4965

Chocolate Cup and Saucer

Per dozen $9 00

No. 4966

Ramikin and Plate

Ramikin, 3½ inches across; plate, 4½ inches

Per dozen $7 15

No. 4967

Croton Set

Soap Dish, Tooth Brush Vase, Handled Mug

Per Set $3 15

For Actual Colors see Colored Insert B, following page 88

LIMOGES ELITE CHINA
No. 7028

Decoration of clusters and bouquets of roses with background in green, leaves in natural color, roses in pink and delicate yellow ; oak leaf border decoration in very delicate green, edges best burnished gold ; clouded gold handles.

No. 4968

Celery Tray

Each $2 10

No. 4970

No. 481—**Pudding Dish and Plate. "Perle"**

Plate 12 inches across, dish 9½ inches across, 3 pieces including fire-proof inner . . . . complete, $7 15

No. 4971

No. 581—**Chop Dish. "Perle"**

12 inches across . . . . each, $3 30

For Actual Colors see Colored Insert B, following page 88

No. 4969

No. 181—**Nut or Berry Bowl**

7½ inches across . . each, $1 10

No. 4972

No. 671—**Plates. "Perle"**

Dinner size, 8½ inches, per dozen, $13 25

Breakfast or entree size, 7½ inches . . per dozen, 11 45

Tea or Dessert size, 6½ inches . . . . per dozen, 9 25

Bread and Butter size, 5½ inches . . . . per dozen, 6 90

ELITE LIMOGES CHINA. No. 7028—Continued

No. 4973

Olive or Bon Bon

5 x 7½ inches . . . . each, $0.65

No. 4975

Ramikins and Plates

Plate 4½ inches across. Ramikins 3½ inches across.

Per doz. $6 50

No. 5974

Condensed Milk Jar. "Perle"

With plate, 5¾ inches across, height of jar 5½ inches.

Complete $2 40

No. 4976

Chocolate Cups and Saucers

Per doz $13 70

No. 4977

Tea Cups and Saucers . per doz., $13 70
A. D. Coffees . . . . . " 10 95

No. 4978

Bouillon Cups and Saucers

Per dozen $15 50

ELITE LIMOGES CHINA. No. 7028—Continued

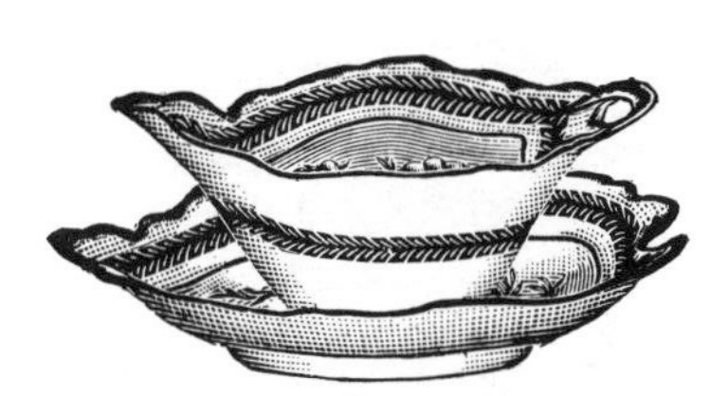

No. 4979

Mayonnaise Dish with Tray

Tray, 6½ x 5⅞ inches ; Dish, 5½ x 4½ inches.

2 pieces, complete $1 80

No. 4980

Cake Plate. "Perle"

10¼ inches from outside to outside of handles

Each $2 00

No. 4981

No. 402—**Footed Comport**

7½ inches across.

Each $3 80

No. 4982

Saucers

Per doz. $6 75

No. 4983

No. 191—**Sugar Bowl and Creamer**

2 pieces $3 50

No. 4984

No. 091—**Tea Pot. "Argent"**

Each $3 00

For Actual Colors see Colored Insert B, following page 88

FINEST LIMOGES CHINA. No. 448

No. 4985

Comport or Berry Bowl on Foot

8 in. across, 3 in. high . . . each, $4 65

Rich dark green border; holly decoration with leaves and berries in natural colors. Gold lace effect over dark green edge, with gold ivy leaves between the holly and the edge; gold traced throughout.

For Actual Colors see Colored Insert B, following page 88

No. 4987

Celery Tray

6½ x 14 inches . . . . each, $3 30

No. 4988

Salad Bowl

10 in. across, 4 in. high . . . each, $4 50

No. 4986

Punch Bowl on Foot

14 inches across, 9 inches high, capacity about 2 gallons. $13 50

No. 4989

Cigar Jar

Top perforated for sponge . . each, $4 50

FINEST LIMOGES CHINA. No. 448—Continued

No. 4990
Sugar Basket
3¼ x 5¾ inches........................each, $2 10

No. 4991
Tea Cup and Saucer
Per doz..............................$19 80

No. 4992
Bon-Bon or Spooner
3¾ x 7 inches..............................each, $1 35

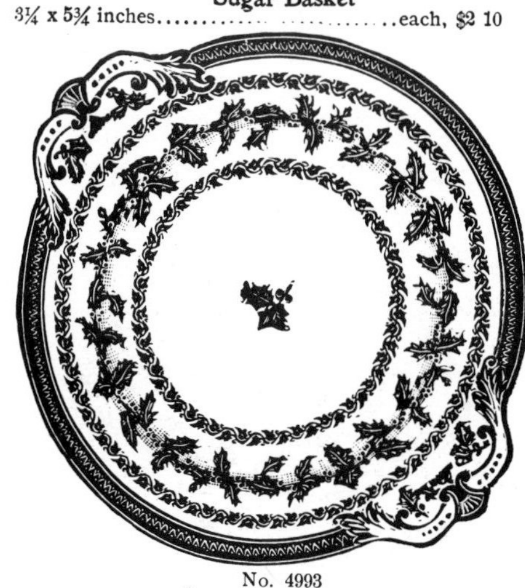

No. 4993
Chop or Round Ice Cream Platter
16 inches from handle to handle............each, $4 50

No. 4994
Plates

7½ inch, entree size........	per doz.		$19 80
6½ " fruit or ice cream	"	"	16 20
5½ " B & B size.......	"	"	13 50

For Actual Colors see Colored Insert B, following page 88

No. 4995
Fancy Tray
15⅛ inches from handle to handle..........each, $5 40

FINEST LIMOGES CHINA

No. 448—Continued

No. 4996

Fancy Brush and Comb Tray

8½ x 13 inches . . . . each, $3 00

No. 4997

Ice Cream Tray

9 x 16½ inches . . . . each, $5 10

No. 4998

Footed Comport or Bon-Bon

6 in. across, 3 in. high

Each $2 40

No. 4999

Tea Pot

Each $3 60

No. 5000

Sugar Bowl

Each $2 40

For Actual Colors see Colored Insert B, following page 88

No. 5001

Creamer

Each $1 65

DECORATION No. 3213

Finest Elite Limoges China

Border decoration of delicate flowers in pink, yellow, purple and green, with border of gold holly each side, beaded edges with best burnished gold.

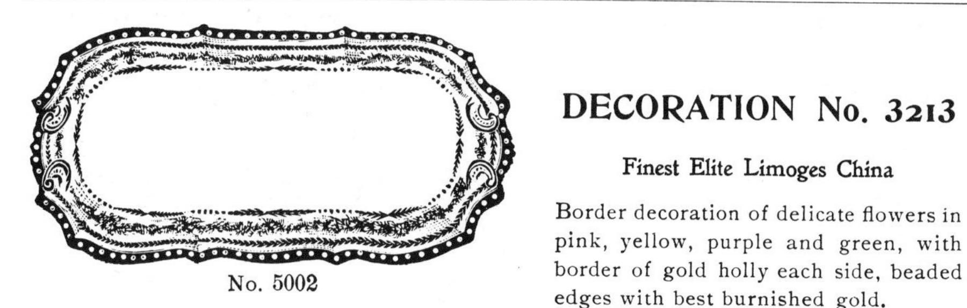

No. 5002

Celery Tray

6 x 12½ inches, each $2 05

No. 5004

Cups and Saucers

Tea Cups and Saucers, per doz.,	$18 20
Coffee " " "	20 10
Bouillon Cups and Saucers "	20 10
A. D. Coffee " " "	14 10

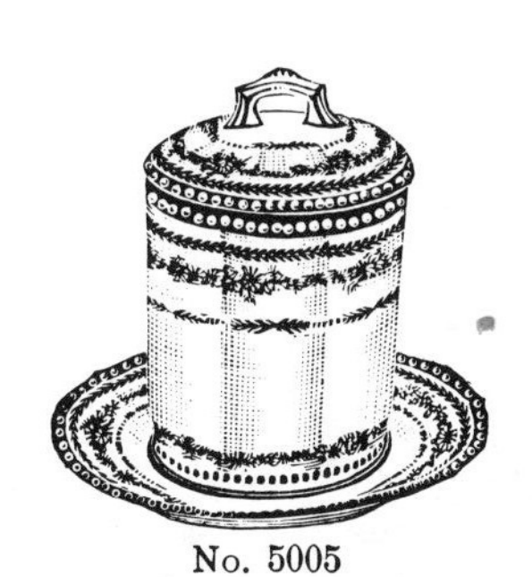

No. 5005

Condensed Milk Jar, with Saucer

5½ inches high, 3½-inch opening.

Complete $2 05

No. 5003

Pudding Dish and Plate

Plate 12½ inches across; Pudding Dish 9½ inches across; 3 pieces, including fireproof Baker.

Complete $6 10

For Actual Colors see Colored Insert C, following page 100

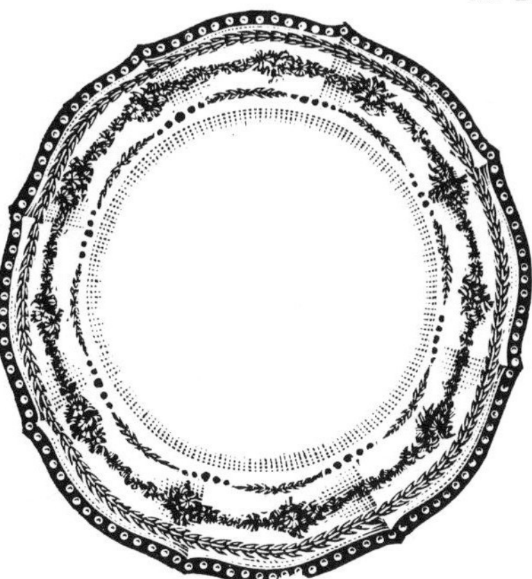

No. 5006

No. 4218.—Plates

Dinner Plates,	8½ in., per doz.,	$17 65
Soup,	" 8 " "	17 35
Breakfast	" 7½ " "	16 30
Tea	" 6½ " "	13 60
B. and B.	" 5½ " "	10 20

DECORATION No. 3213—Continued

No. 5007

Tea Pot

5½ inches high . . . . each, $3 05

No. 5008

Sugar and Creamer

4½ inches high . . . . two pieces, $3 75

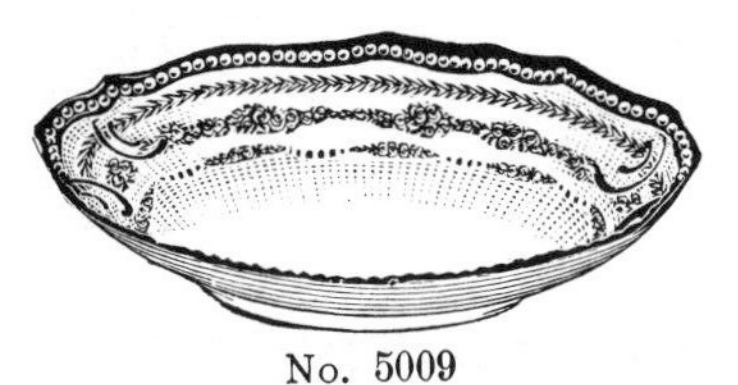

No. 5009

Oval Bon Bon or Spoon-Holder

5 x 7½ inches . . . each, $0 90

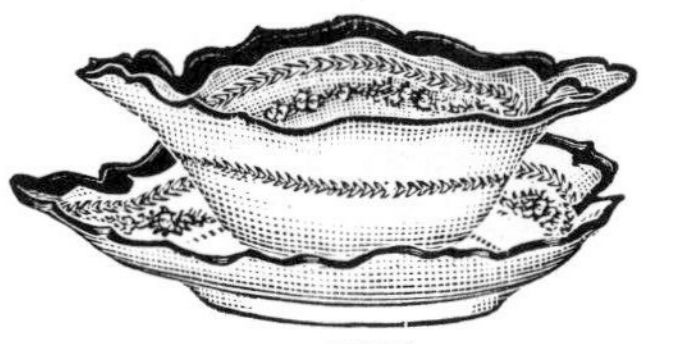

No. 5010

Mayonnaise Dressing Bowl

Bowl, 4¼ x 5¾ inches.

Stand, 5¾ x 6½ inches.

2 pieces, complete . . . $2 35

No. 5011

Covered Bon Bon

5 inches across . each, $1 95

No. 5012

Hair Receiver

4½ in. across . . each, $1 50

For Actual Colors see Insert C, following page 100

FINEST "ELITE" LIMOGES CHINA DECORATION. No. 44

Border decoration in bunches of lavender and yellow flowers, connecting with sage green leaves. A lustre border edge and line on shoulder, with gold lace work over the lustre effect. Also shoulder line of flowers with sprays of flowers in center.

No. 5013

Low Comport or Fruit Dish

8½ x 10½ inches . . . . . . each, $1 95

No. 5014

Plates

8 in. or entree size,	per doz.,	$13 20
7½ " or dessert size,	"	11 85
6 " or ice cream size,	"	8 55
5½ " or B. & B. size,	"	6 90

No. 5015

Cracker Jar

6½ inches high . . . . each, $3 00

No. 5016

Fernery

7¼ inch opening, 4⅜ inches high, with porcelain inner . . . . . each, $4 80

For Actual Colors see Colored Insert D, following page 122

No. 5017

Celery Tray

5¾ x 13½ inches. . . . . each, $2 40

ELITE LIMOGES CHINA

No. 44—Continued

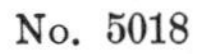

No. 5018

Salad Bowl

11 inches across.

Each $2 70

No. 5020

Comport or Fruit Dish

9 inches across.

Each $1 95

No. 5019

Ice Cream Tray

11 x 16½ inches.

Each $3 30

No. 5021

Pudding Dish and Plate

Plate 12½ inches across; Pudding Dish 9¼-inch opening.

3 pieces with fireproof baker.

Per set $6 00

No. 5022

Condensed Milk Jar

With Plate.

3½-inch opening ; 5¾ inches across plate.

Complete $2 40

For Actual Colors see Colored Insert D, following page 122

ELITE LIMOGES CHINA. No. 44—Continued

No. 5023

Tea Pot

6 inches high.

Each $2 80

No. 5024

Sugar and Cream

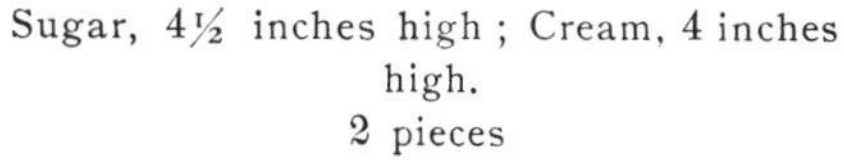

Sugar, 4½ inches high ; Cream, 4 inches high.

2 pieces

Per set $3 20

No. 5025

Brush and Comb Tray

8 x 12 inches . . . . each, $1 95

No. 5026

Croton Set

Covered Soap Dish, Tooth Brush Mug, Handled Mug, 3 pieces, complete $3 30

For Actual Colors see Colored Insert D, following page 122

ELITE LIMOGES CHINA. No. 44—Continued

No. 5027
Mayonnaise Dish with Tray
2 pieces $1 75

No. 5030
Ramikin and Plate
Ramikin, 3½ inches across; plate, 4¾ inches across
Per doz $8 15

No. 5033
Individual Olive or Bon Bon Dish
3¼ x 4½ inches. . . . . . . .each, $0 40

No. 5028
Bon Bon or Jelly Dish with feet
6¾ inches across . . . . each, $1 40

No. 5031
Cake Plate
10¼ inches from outside to outside edge of handles....each, $2 10

No. 5034
Cups and Saucers
Tea Cups . . . . per doz. $14 40
A. D. Cups . . . . " " 12 00

No. 5029
Hair Receiver
3 inches high, with opening in top to receive hair . . . . . . each, $1 50

No. 5032
Olive or Bon Bon Dish
4¾ x 7¾ inches. . . . . . each, $0 70

No. 5035
Pickle or Radish Dish
5⅞ x 8 inches . . . . each, $1 35

For Actual Colors see Colored Insert D, following page 122

DRESDEN CHINA

Characteristic Dresden flower decoration in bouquets of scattered flowers and gold sun-ray edges.

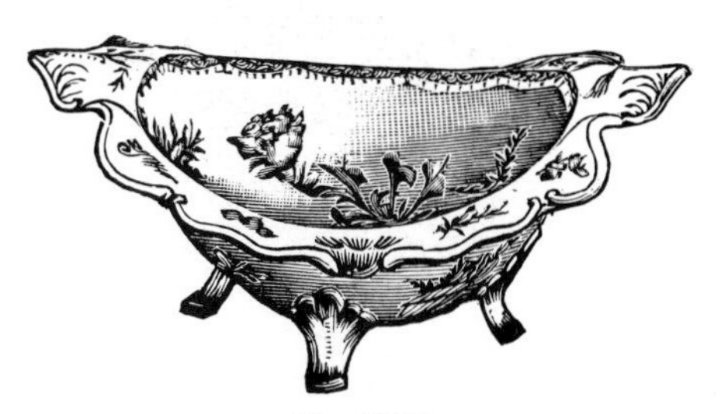

No. 5036

No. 4224—**Fancy Dish**

Suitable for bon bons, radishes, nuts, etc.

6½ x 8½. . . . . .each, $3 25
Large size, 11 inches wide. . . . " 4 85

No. 5037

No. 8374—**Egg Dish**

For serving boiled eggs

8½ inches across. . . . each, $2 30

No. 5038

No. 2724—**Oval Bon Bon**

Also nice for short stemmed flowers

6 inches across. . . . . .each, $1 15

No. 5039

No. 9494—**Berry Dish. Perforated Bottom**

Plate, 9¾ inches across. Dish, 9¾ inches, 2 pieces, complete $4 25

For Actual Colors see Colored Insert H, following page 206

No. 5040

No. 7983—**Egg Dish**

For serving eggs

14 inches long . . . . each, $3 90

DRESDEN CHINA
(Continued)

No. 5041

No. 9094—**Mustard or Horse Radish Jar**

Each $1 30

No. 5044

No. 1334—**Lemon or Orange Squeezer**

Each $1 30

No. 5646

No. 0094—**Hot Water or Milk Jar**

Each, with plate $2 95

No. 5042

No. 8524—**Covered Cheese Dish**

Size of bottom 8 x 10½

Each $5 85

No. 5047

No. 2884—**Shaving Mug**

Each $1 65

For Actual Colors see Colored Insert H, following page 206

No. 5043

No. 7704—**Covered Egg Dish**

6 x 7¼ inches . . . . each, $3 90

No. 5045

No. 7474—**Olive or Bon Bon**

5¾ inches across

Each $1 00

No. 5048

No. 3853—**Mayonnaise Dish**

Also good for horse radish. Plate 8 inches across.

Each $2 95

No. 5049

No. 195-82—**Chocolate Pot**

Large size . . . . . . each, $1 25
Small size . . . . . . " 1 00

BAVARIAN CHINA

ORLEANS, DECORATION 289-805

Border decoration with festoons of delicate pink flowers and green leaves; two lines of gold around edge.

No. 5051

No. 195-92—**Cracker Jar**

5 inches high

Each $0 75

No. 5052

No. 195-73—**Condensed Milk Jar with Plate**

Complete $0 50

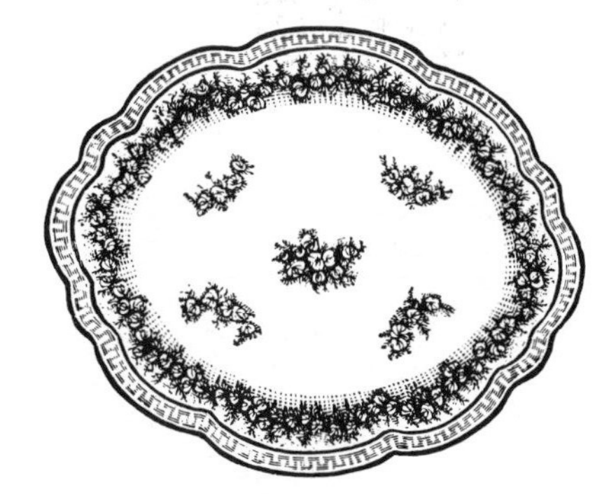

No. 5050

No. 195-83—**Brush and Comb Tray**

9½ x 11½ inches

Each $0.75

No. 5053

No. 195-63—**Syrup with Plate**

Complete $0 50

BAVARIAN CHINA. No. 289-805—Continued

No. 5054

No. 195—**Bouillon Cups and Saucers**

Per dozen $4 00

Coffee Cups and Saucers, per doz., $4 00

After Dinners . . . . . " 2 80

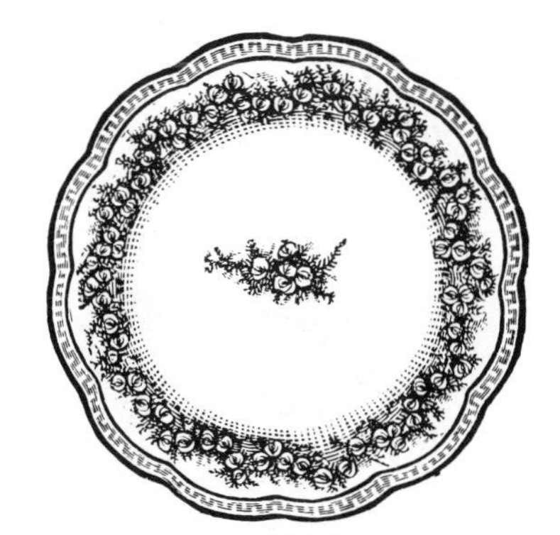

No. 5057

Plate

Dinner, 8½ inches . .	per doz.,	$3 20
Soup, 8 inches	"	3 20
Breakfast, 7½ inches .	"	2 50
Tea, 6½ inches	"	2 00
B. and B., 5½ inches .	"	1 75

No. 5055

No. 195 L.-14—**Trinket Set**

Consisting of Brush and Comb Tray, 1 Powder Box, 1 Pomade Box, 1 Ring Stand, 1 Hairpin Tray.

Complete $1 50

No. 5058

No. 195-61—**Mustard or Horse Radish Dish, with Spoon**

Each $0 25

No. 5056

No. 755-805—**Tea Caddy**

5 inches high. . . . each, $0.30

No. 5059

No 195-81—**Bone Plates**

Per dozen $2 40

BAVARIAN CHINA. No. 289-805.—Continued

No. 5060

No. 191-83—Teapot, Sugar and Cream, small size, 3 pieces $0 70

CHOCOLATE SETS*

No. 5061

Chocolate Set. "Regence"

No. 843—Finest Elite Limoges China. Body of China in either yellow, salmon or light green. Watteau (small figure) decoration. Fully decorated in best burnished gold. Handles solid gold.

1 Tray, 6 Cups and Saucers, 1 Chocolate Jug.

Complete $23 00

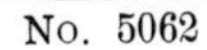

No. 5062

Chocolate Set

Austrian China. Trays, cups and saucers, and chocolate pot, having portraits of celebrated court beauties. Solid gold handles. Maroon, green or blue, with gold lace decoration.

Tray, 6 Cups and Saucers, Chocolate Jug.

Complete $18 10

*Shown in case, page 228

AUSTRIAN IMPERIAL CROWN CHINA. No. 7444

Decorated with large roses in yellow, with leaves in natural color. Edge maroon with gold lace and fancy gold border below maroon band. Handles traced gold.

No. 5063

Salad Bowl "Wettin"

9½ inches across, 2¾ deep . . . each, $1 35

No. 5065

Cracker Jar. "Estelle"

6½ inches high . . . . each, $1 70

No. 5066

Pudding Dish and Plate. "Estelle"

Plate 11 inches across; pudding dish 8½, three pieces, including fireproof inner $3 50

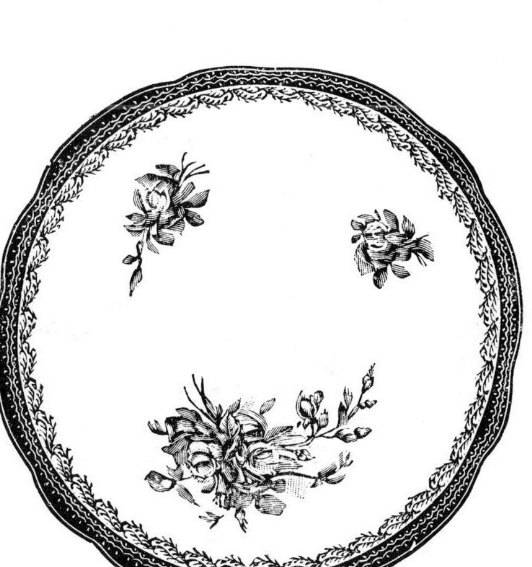

No. 5064

Chop Dish. "Estelle"

13 inches across $2 00

Plates. No. 5067

Dinner size 8½ inch, per doz. $6 50

Breakfast or entree, size 7½, per doz 5 50

Tea or Dessert, size 6½ inch, per doz 4 50

Bread and Butter, size 5½ inch, per doz 3 50

IMPERIAL CROWN CHINA No. 7444—Continued

No. 5068

No. 77½. **Creamer**

Each $0 60

No. 5069

No. 77½. **Sugar Bowl**

Each $1 00

No. 5070

Tea Pot. No. 2

Each $1 25

No. 5071

Rose Bowl

4 in. high, 2 in. opening

Each $0 70

No. 5072

Cake or Bread Plate. "Estelle"

10½ inches from handle to handle . each, $1 00

No. 5073

Cups and Saucers

Tea Cups and Saucers, per dozen $6 00

A. D. Coffee Cups and Saucers per dozen 5 25

No. 5074

Fancy Tray. "Stail"

8 x 11¼ . . . . each, $1 50

IMPERIAL CROWN CHINA. No. 7444—Continued

No. 5075

Covered Muffin Dish or Cake Dish

9½ inches across plate . . . . . each $1 75

No. 5078

Tea Pot Tile

6½ inches across . . . . each $0 45

No. 5079

Ice Bowl

Each $1 50

No. 5077

Fernery "Burges"

7½ inches across, 5 inches high, with inner

Complete $2 80

No, 5076

No. 252—**Berry Set. "Estelle"**

1 Bowl, 12 Saucers

13 pieces $4 25

No. 5080

Footed Olive or Bon Bon

No. 3, 6 inches across . . . each $0 85

No. 7, 7½ inches across . . " 1 40

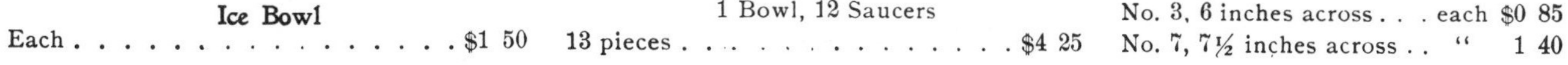

FINEST LIMOGES CHINA. No. 0111

No. 5081

Ice Bowl with Plate

Bowl 6¾ inches across.

2 pieces, complete $4 50

Apple blossom decoration in pink, with light green on a background of dark green; edges best burnished gold.

No. 5083

Celery Tray

Size 6¼ x 13½

Each $2 85

No. 5082

Plates

7½-inch, entree size. $16 20
6½-in., ice cream or dessert size 13 50
5-inch, bread and butter size . . 11 15

For Actual Colors see Colored Insert C, following page 100

No. 5084

Salad Bowl

9½ inches across, 4½ inches high

Each $3 75

No. 5085

Covered Muffin or Hot Cake Dish

9½ inches across plate

Each $3 60

LIMOGES CHINA No. 0111

(Continued)

No. 5086

Cake Dish

Open handles, 11 inches from outside to outside . . . . each, $2 70

No. 5089

Horse Radish Dish

4½ inches high $2 25

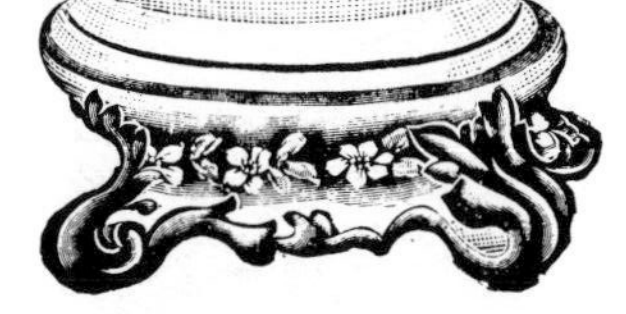

No. 5087

Punch Bowl on Stand

14 inches across, 9 inches high, capacity about 2½ gallons $15 00

For Actual Colors see Colored Insert C, following page 100

No. 5088

Mayonnaise Dish

5½ inches across. $1 80

No. 5090

Tea Strainer with Bottom

2 pieces, complete $2 10

No. 5091

Oval Olive or Bon Bon

4¾ x 6¾ inches. . . . . . . each, $1 05

LIMOGES CHINA
No. 0111
(Continued)

No. 5092
Tea Pot
5¾ inches high . . . . each, $3 60

No. 5095
Black Coffee Pot
9½ inches high . . . . each, $4 50

No. 5093
Sugar Bowl
6¾ inches from outside to outside of handles. . . . . each, $2 40

No. 5096
Ice Cream or Berry Saucers
5¾ inches across . . . . per doz., $11 70

For Actual Colors see Colored Insert C, following page 100

No. 5094
Creamer
4¼ inches high . . . . each, $1 50

No. 5097
Covered Mustard
3 inches high . . . . each, $1 65

LIMOGES CHINA. No. 0111—Continued

No. 5098

Covered Cracker or Biscuit Jar

8½ inches from outside to outside of handles ; 4 inches high

Each $4 50

No. 5099—Chop or Round Ice Cream Tray
13½ inches across . . . . each, $3 75

No. 5100

Fernery on Feet

7 inch opening, 4½ inches high with porcelain inner, complete . . . $4 50

No. 5101

A. D. Coffee Cup

Also large enough for chocolate

Dozen $16 20

No. 5102—Tea Cups and Saucers

Dozen. $18 00

No. 5103

Bouillon Cups and Saucers

Dozen $21 60

For Actual Colors see Colored Insert C, following page 100

CAULDON CHINA

No. 3702—Dresden Decoration

Embossed basket effect, border with bouquets of flower decoration in pink, purple and sage green leaves; flower decoration on shoulder, and fancy flower center; gold edge and gold lines.

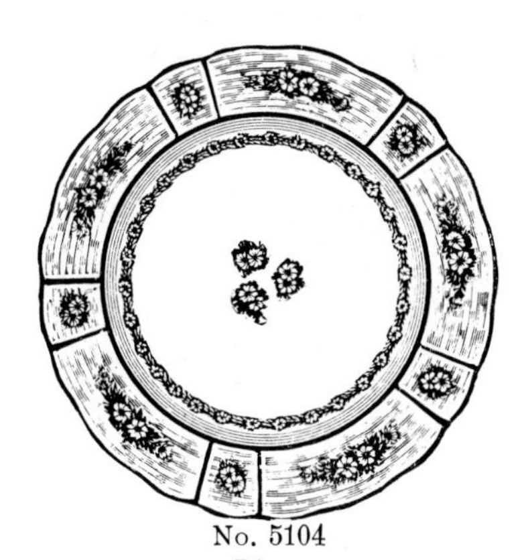

No. 5104

Plates

Dinner size, 10 inch . dozen,		$21 60
Entree or Breakfast size, 8 inch	"	19 20
Tea size, 7 inch . . .	"	16 20
Pie or Ice Cream size, 6 inch	"	13 20
Bread and Butter size, 5 inch	"	10 20

No. 5107

Tea Pot

Each. $4 05

No. 5105—Chop Platter

12 inches across $6 20

No. 5108—Sugar

Each $3 45

No. 5106—Tea Cups and Saucers

Per dozen $19 20
Bouillon Cups . . per doz. 22 80

No. 5109—Jug

Size 24 . . . . $2 85
" 30 . . . . 2 40
" 36 . . . . 1 70

No. 5110—Creamer

Each $2 40

D 089—"BIARRITZ"

Finest Limoges China. Border of festoons and garlands in delicate pink, yellow and blue flowers. Green leaves. Sage green Rococo border Rosette center of flowers.

The combination and blending of the colors in this combination is particularly delicate and very handsome.

For Actual Colors see Colored Insert A, following page 78

No. 5111

Ice Tub, with Drainer

5½ inches across, 5¾ inches high

Each, complete............................$2 60

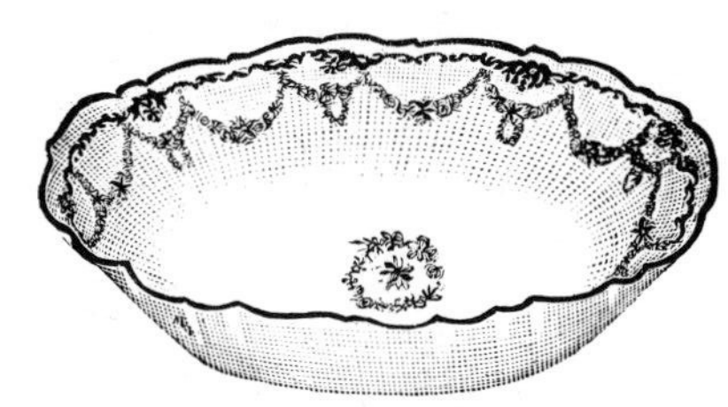

No. 5114

Compotier. Low, deep

5½ inches across	each	$0 30
6¾ " "	"	50
8¼ " "	"	1 00
10 " "	"	1 35

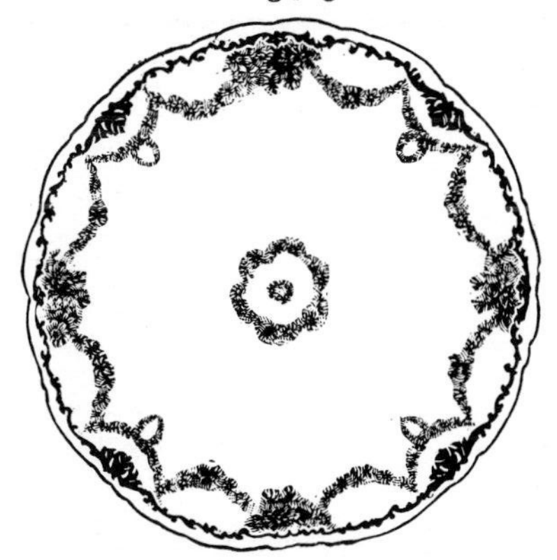

No. 5112—Plates

Entree, 8-inch	per doz.	$5 25
Dessert, 7-inch	"	4 70
Ice Cream, 6-inch	"	3 45
Bread and Butter, 5-inch	"	3 00

No. 5115—Bouillon Cup and Saucer

Per dozen...$7 60

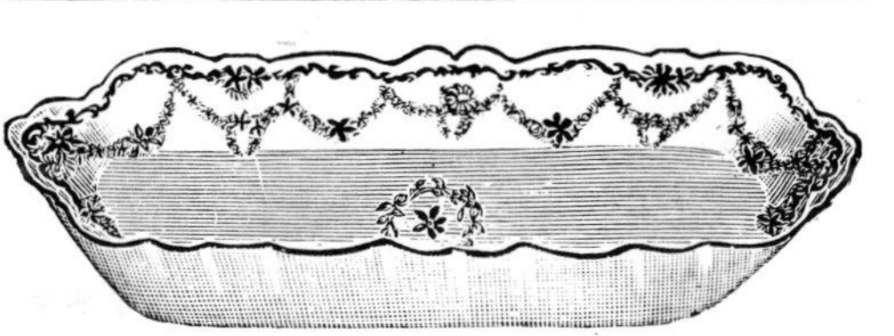

No. 5113

Celery Tray

5½ x 12½ inches.................................each $1 35

No. 5116

Jugs

3 Pints, (No. 1)	each	$2 60
2 " (No. 2)	"	1 40
1 " (No. 3)	"	1 05

DRESDEN CHINA. B. U. No. 427

Solid Cobalt Blue with small figures in panel decoration, edges and all embossed parts traced with gold.

No. 5117
Envelope and Paper Rack
3 x 6½ inches.
2 compartments
Each $4 00

No. 5120
Rolling Blotter
2½ x 4½ inches
Each $1 45

No. 5121
Pen Wiper, with Bristles
Each $1 00

No. 5118
Writing Desk Pad with Blotter and China Corners
10 x 16 inches
Each $2 90

For Actual Colors see Colored Insert H, following page 206

No. 5119
Envelope or Postal Card Holder
2½ x 4 inches. 5 inches high
Each $2 50

No. 5122
Seal
3½ inches long
Each $1 50

Prices for engraving initial monogram quoted on request.

No. 5123
Covered Ink Stand
2½ inches square
Each $1 25

DRESDEN CHINA. B. U. No. 427—Continued

For Actual Colors see Colored Insert H, following page 206

No. 5124

Paper File

6 inches tall . . . each, $1 15

No. 5125

Calendar Stand

With celluoid cards, 2½ inches high $1 25

No. 5126

Sponge Cup

2½ inch opening, each, $1 15

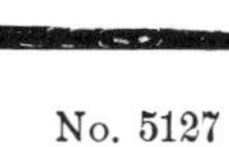

No. 5127

Pen Holder

7 inches long . . . . each, $0 85

No. 5128

Candlestick for Sealing Wax

2¾ x 4 inches, each, $1 00

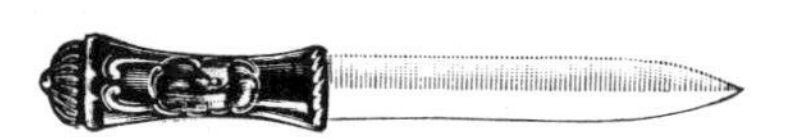

No. 5129

Paper Cutter

8½ inches long . . . . . .each, $1 10

No. 5130

Candlestick for Sealing Wax

3½ inches across, each, $0 85

No. 5131

Postage Stamp Box

3 compartments, each, $1 15

DESK NOVELTIES

DRESDEN CHINA, 04D

With delicate cream and salmon background and flower decoration in combined tints of pink, yellow, blue with green leaves, edges traced in gold. This decoration is very similar to the celebrated Royal Worcester pattern

For Actual Colors see Colored Insert H, following page 206

No. 5132

No. 9851—**Calendar with Celluloid Dates**

4 inches high, 2½ inches across

Each $0 95

No. 5134

No. 0481-04.—**Rolling Blotter**

5½ x 3 inches

Each $0 90

No. 5133

No. 6981.—**Writing Desk Pad with Blotter and China Corners**

12 x 16 inches . . . . each, $1 25

No. 5135

No. 8581-04.—**Seal**

Each $0 70

No. 5136

No. 5181-04—**Candlestick for Sealing Wax**

3½ inches across . . each, $0 50

DRESDEN CHINA, 04D—Continued

For Actual Colors see Colored Insert H, following page 206

No. 5137

No. 1681-04—**Paper File**

6 inches high . . . . each, $0 70

No. 5138

No. 3881-04—**Envelope and Paper Rack**

3 x 5 x 5½ inches high, 2 compartments.

Each $2 45

No. 5139

No. 4681-04—**Ink Stand and Pen Holder Combined**

5 inches wide, 8 inches long.

Each $1 75

No. 5140

No. 0102-04—**Pen Holder**

Each $0 50

No. 5141

No. 4191-04—**Stamp Box**

3½ x 1¾ inches . . . . . . each, $0 70

No. 5142

No. 1481-04—**Pen Wiper with Bristles**

Each $0 50

FRENCH VASES

We carry a very large assortment of these goods, both larger and smaller, and will gladly furnish full description and prices on application.

No. 5143

No. 1712—**Sevres Vase**

French figure decoration, in the prevailing tints of either pink, yellow or empire green, with ormolu mountings.

Height, 6¾ inches

Each $3 85

No. 5144

No. 6302—**Sevres Vase**

French figure decoration, in the prevailing tints of either pink, yellow, or empire green, with ormolu mountings.

No, 1,	10 inches high,	$10 50
" 2,	9 " "	8 25
" 3,	8 " "	6 60
" 4,	7 " "	4 15

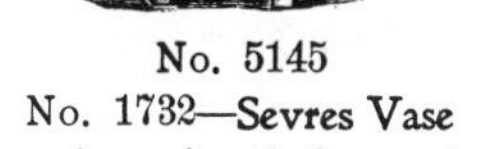

No. 5145

No. 1732—**Sevres Vase**

Handsomely painted figure decoration, with raised paste gold. Rich ormolu mountings.

Height, 15 inches . . . . . . each, **$13 75**

No. 5146

No. 6412—**Sevres Vase**

Heavy ormolu mounting; rich figure decoration.

No. 2,	16½ inch high,	$12 40
" 3,	14½ " "	10 70
" 4,	13 " "	7 90

No. 5147

No. 4591—**Sevres Vase**

Figure decoration with flowers, etc.; edges pink, blue, or empire green; ormolu mountings

Height, **6** inches

Each $3 00

VIENNA

No. 5148

Vienna Vase

Rich maroon and cream decoration with paste gold; solid gold handles. Hand-painted figure decoration on both sides of body.

Height, 14½ inches

Price $24 00

No. 5149

Vienna Plate. "Listening"

Richly decorated by hand. Border in delicate tints of pink, cream and maroon, with raised paste gold.

9½ inches across

Price $20 00

We carry constantly in stock a large variety of these plates in different subjects, which we would be pleased to describe upon application.

No. 5150

Vienna Vase

Rich maroon and cream decoration with paste gold. Hand-painted figure decoration on both sides of body. Solid gold handles.

Height, 13½ inches

Price **$26 50**

DUTCH POTTERY

Green body. Very high glaze.
Shapes very quaint.

No. 5151
Umbrella Shape Vase
14½ inches high . . . . . each, $2 50

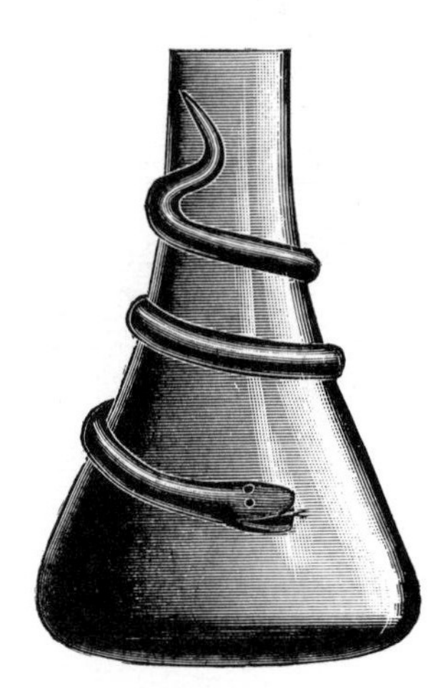

No. 5152
Serpentine Vase
10¼ inches high . . . . . each, $1 60

No. 5153
Pitcher
No. 81—13 inches high . . each, $1 60

DUTCH POTTERY VASES—Continued

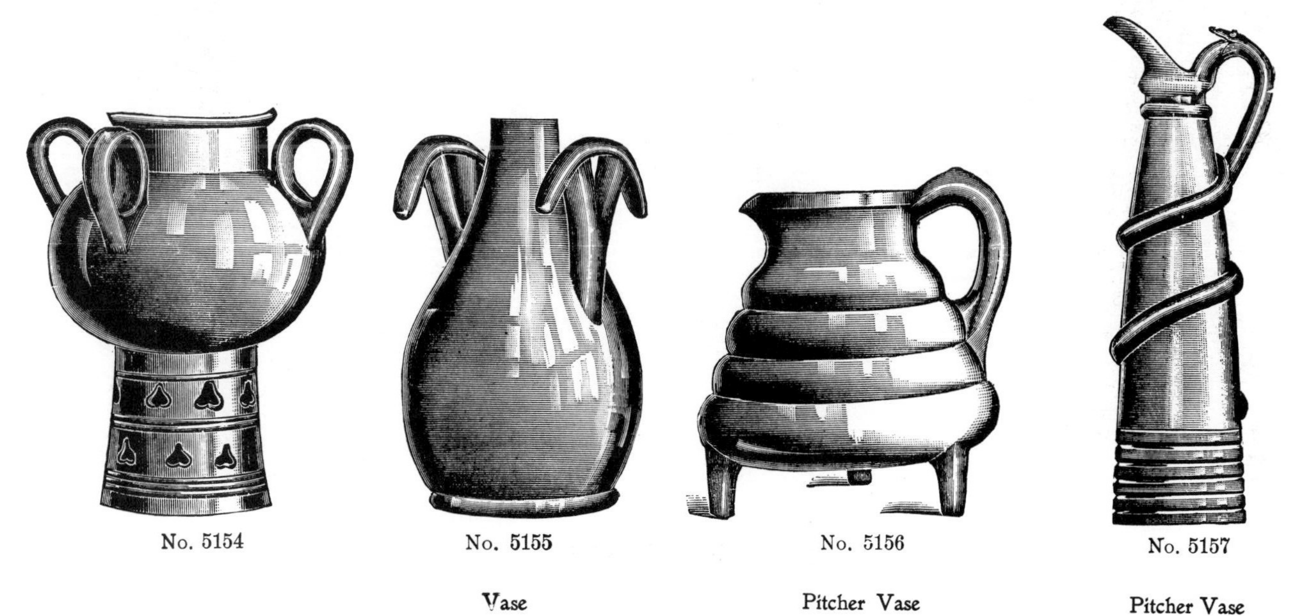

No. 5154

No. 41—9½ in. high, each, $1.30

No. 5155

Vase

No. 42—9⅜ in. high, each, $1.30

No. 5156

Pitcher Vase

7½ inches high . each, $1.30

No. 5157

Pitcher Vase

No. 5—11¾ in. high, each, $0.95

DUTCH POTTERY VASES—Continued

No. 5158 No. 5159 No. 5160 No. 5161

Candlestick

No.51—6¼ in. high, each, $0.45 7½ inches high . . each, $0.45 No.32—8½ in. high, each, $0.95 No.02—9½ in. high, each, $0.65

DRESDEN CLOCKS

No. 5162

Dresden Clock

Delicate Dresden decoration, or dresden blue, with raised flowers and gold work throughout; the clock is 11 inches high, has eight-day movement, with cathedral gong.

Each $11 50

No. 5164

French Traveling Clock

Gilt and beveled glass frame, best works; ivory dial, with plush-lined leatherette case. Eight-day movement.

Complete $6 50

No. 5163

No. 3016—**Dresden Clock**

Raised flowers and traced gold, in delicate Dresden decoration, or Dresden blue, 36-hour movement, 8½ inches high.

Each $4 50

HALL CLOCKS

A branch of our business which of late has assumed remarkable proportions, is that of Hall Clocks.

This is largely on account of the modern style of architecture, which in artistic houses gives so much prominence to the hall and stairway. Such a residence can hardly be considered furnished without a clock of this description. The supply of genuine old "grandfather's" clocks having become exhausted, those of a better make, more complete, and much more ornamental, are now demanded.

Our trade in these clocks has become so important as to warrant us in entering into what is practically their manufacture, although we do not, as yet, make the works. We are able, however, by assembling the parts ourselves, to furnish clocks to order, or otherwise, in any style, any wood, any finish, or any architecture to match interiors.

No single piece of furniture can add more to the dignity and nobility of a residence than one of these great Hall Clocks encased in mahogany or antique oak, softly striking melodious chimes each quarter hour, and the full or half hour on a grand, solemn, low-toned Cathedral gong.

Hitherto the grade of clocks we offer have been handled principally by concerns to whom large profits are a matter of course. Consequently, our prices for Hall Clocks are, compared with theirs, much more than

"One Quarter Less than Elsewhere."

HALL CLOCK

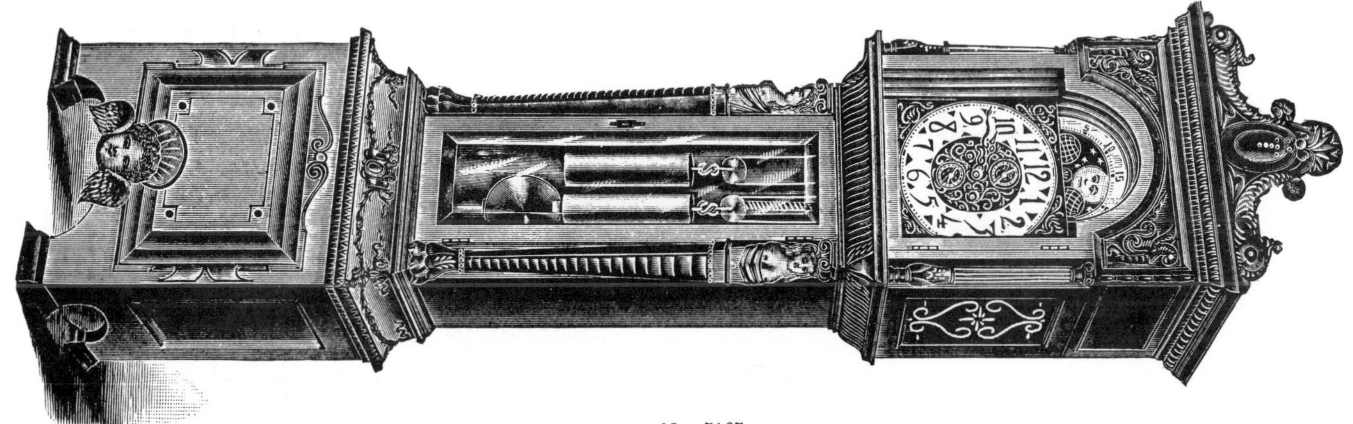

No. 5165

Hall Clock

Richly hand-carved case, steel dials with pierced brass figures; can be had in antique oak, mahogany or Flemish oak; size at base 22 x 15¼ inches; height, 7 feet 6 inches. Fitted with hour and half hour movement, striking on Cathedral gong.

Price $200 00

Fitted with Westminster movement, striking the hour on Cathedral gong, on chimes each quarter.

Price $290 00

Fitted with Westminster and Whittington movement with hour strike on Cathedral gong and chimes each quarter; can be regulated to either Westminster chimes on 4 gong, or Whittington movement on 8 bells.

Price $300 00

HALL CLOCK

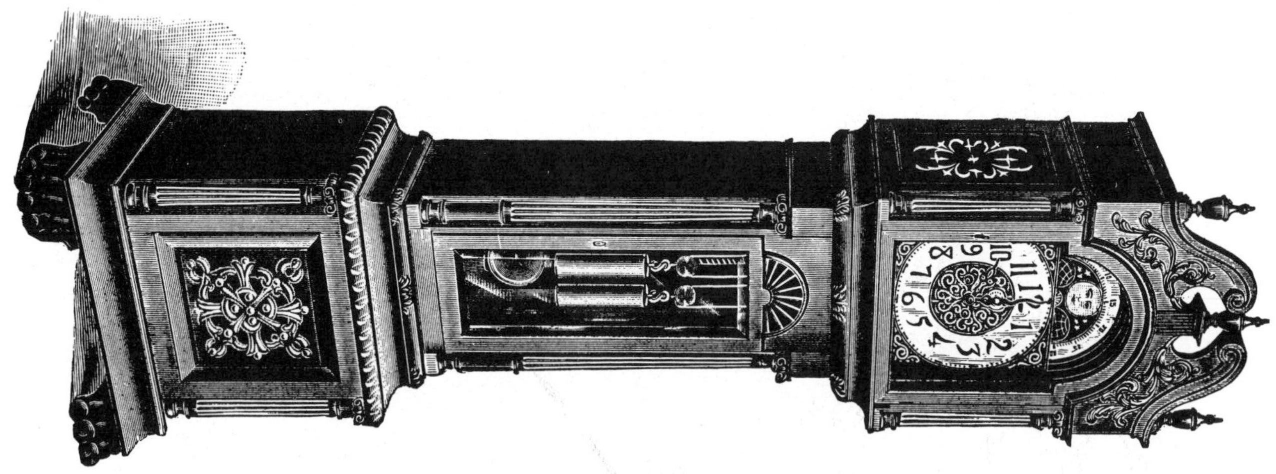

No. 5166

Hall Clock, H. & S.

Steel dials with raised pierced figures; can be had in antique oak, mahogany or Flemish oak. Size at base 24½ x 16 inches, height, 7 feet 11 inches. Fitted with hour and half hour Cathedral gong, 8 day movement.

Price $150 00

Fitted with Westminster chimes striking hourly, and chimes each quarter hour.

Price $210 00

Fitted with Westminster and Whittington movement striking the hours on Cathedral gong; chimes each quarter hour on Westminster 4 gong, or on Whittington movement on 8 bells. Can be regulated to either movement by turning indicator on the dial.

Price $230 00

IN ART DEPARTMENT

CAMEO VASES, PLAQUES, Etc.

Background in dull finish sage green; figures in relief in white. They are all arranged for hanging.

No. 5167
No. 7237—11 inches across................. $5 10

No. 5169
No. 8477—13½ x 7½ inches.................. $6 00

No. 5168
No. 1377—13 x 11½ inches........................ $6 60

No. 5170
No. 8718—10½ x 8 inches.................... $4 50

No. 5171
No. 2437—11 x 6½ inches.................... $3 90

For Actual Colors see Colored Insert H, following page 206

CAMEO WARE

(Continued)

No. 5172

No. 7077—12½ x 11 inches....................$5 10

No. 5173

No. 8377—14 x 10½ inches.......................$9 60

No. 5174

No. 5377—9 x 8 inches........................$3 45

No. 5175

No. 6177—9 x 7½ inches......................$2 70

For Actual Colors see Colored Insert H, following page 206

No. 5176

No. 4177—8¾ x 7 inches......................$3 15

CAMEO WARE—Continued

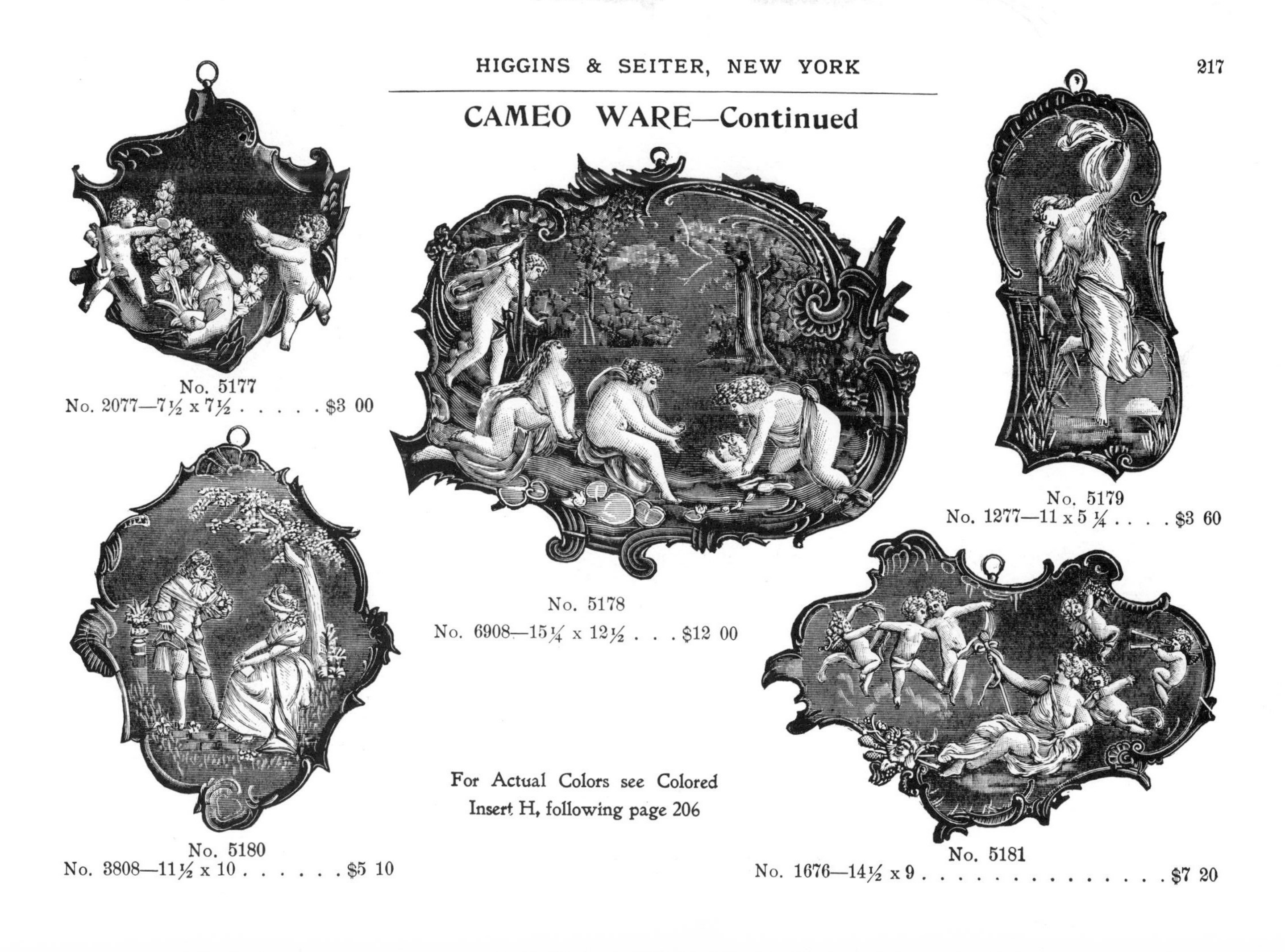

No. 5177
No. 2077—7½ x 7½ $3 00

No. 5178
No. 6908—15¼ x 12½ . . . $12 00

No. 5179
No. 1277—11 x 5¼ $3 60

No. 5180
No. 3808—11½ x 10 . . . . . . $5 10

For Actual Colors see Colored Insert H, following page 206

No. 5181
No. 1676—14½ x 9 . . . . $7 20

CAMEO WARE—Continued

For Actual Colors see Colored Insert H,
following page 206

No. 5182

No. 5167—6¼ x 6 . . . . $1 00

No. 5183

No. 2267—5 x 5 . . . . $0 60

No. 5184

No. 1077—6¼ x 6¾ $1 35

No. 5185

No. 7567—4¾ inches high $0 80

No. 5186

No. 0077—6 x 5½ $1 50

No. 5187

No. 3357—4½ inches high $0 60

CAMEO WARE—Continued

For Actual Colors see Colored Insert H, following page 206

No. 5188
No. 1767—6 inches high . . . $1 65

No. 5189
No. 6437—8 x 6½ . . $2 10

No. 5190
No. 2467—7 in. high . $1 50
9½ " 2 25

No. 5192
No. 5297—8½ high, $2 40

No. 5191
No. 0167—10 x 6 . . . . $3 60

No. 5193
No. 0267—9 x 4½ $3 00

PLATES

No. 5194

Plate. Limoges

Beautiful dark blue underglaze rim, with gold lace border and gold center.

	Per doz.
Entree size	$18 10
Dinner or soup size	23 00

Plate. Limoges

Underglaze dark blue (or white) rim, incrusted gold edge, gold center.

Blue and Gold	Per doz.
Dinner	$31 95
Breakfast	26 45
Soup	30 45
Bread and Butter	16 10

White and Gold	Per doz.
Dinner	$23 35
Breakfast	19 25
Soup	22 70
Bread and Butter	12 15

No. 5195

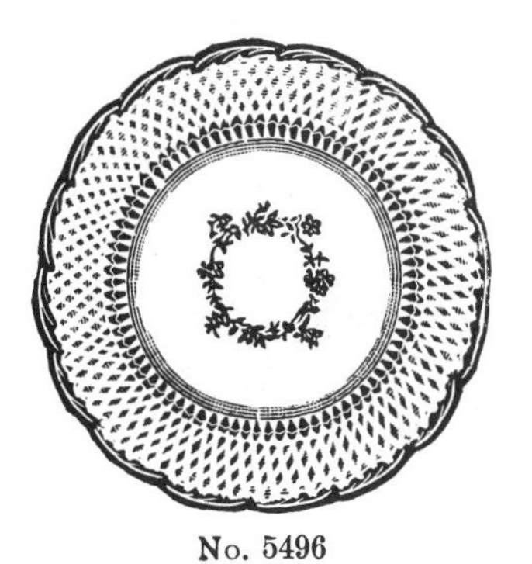

No. 5496

G—7437

Plate. Minton

Border of raised turquoise dots, flower center, gold edge.

	Per doz.
Dinner	$34 80
Breakfast	29 90
Soup	34 50
Tea,	24 15
Bread and Butter	18 40

Limoges China Plate

Border decoration in either pink, blue, green or maroon; two rows of flowers in delicate pink, blue and green leaves; two rows of gold lace with fancy gold over the colored edges.

		Per doz.
Dinner Plate,	8½-inch,	$18 00
Breakfast or Entree	7½ "	16 80
Tea or Dessert,	6½ "	13 20
B. and B.,	5½ "	9 60

No. 5197

BREAD AND BUTTER PLATES

No. 5198

No. 197-84—Bread and Butter Plate "Turgot"

Finest Elite Limoges China; cream edge, with two rows of burnished gold, and very delicate green tint between the gold; fancy gold star center.
Per dozen $11 25

For Actual Colors see Colored Insert G, following page 164

No. 5199

No. 2912—Bread and Butter Plate

English Wedgwood. Border flower decoration in delicate pink and yellow flowers, green and gold leaves. Heavily decorated in the best burnished gold throughout.
Per dozen $14 80

For Actual Colors see Colored Insert F. following page 154

No. 5200

No. 2682—Bread and Butter Plate "Rouen"

Haviland's Limoges China. Border decoration in delicate green flowers with hair brown and lavender edge; border of small flowers on shoulder of plate and fancy rosette center; clouded burnished gold edges.
Per dozen $5 50

For Actual Colors see Colored Insert D, following page 122

No. 5201

No. 9416—Bread and Butter Plate. "Perle"

Elite Limoges China. Rococo and flower border decoration in sage green and light green with flowers in pink; fancy center; clouded gold edge.
Per dozen $4 10

For Actual Colors see Colored Insert B, following page 88

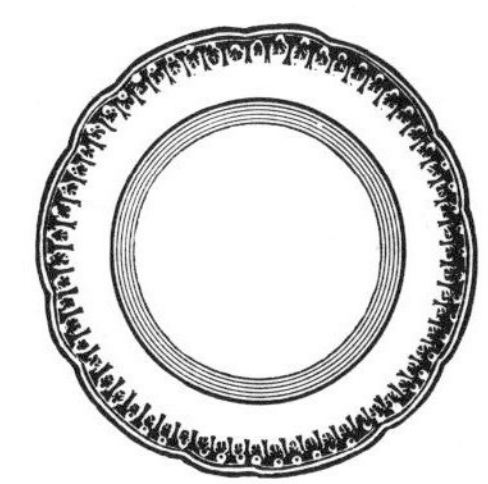

No. 5202

No. 7843—Bread and Butter Plate

Limoges China, lace gold border, gold line on shoulder.
Per dozen $3 40

For Actual Colors see Colored Insert A, following page 78

No. 5203

No. 2674—Bread and Butter Plate Wedgwood "Brighton"

Underglazed blue fancy border with gold.
Per dozen $11 70

For Actual Colors see Colored Insert D, following page 122

OYSTER PLATES

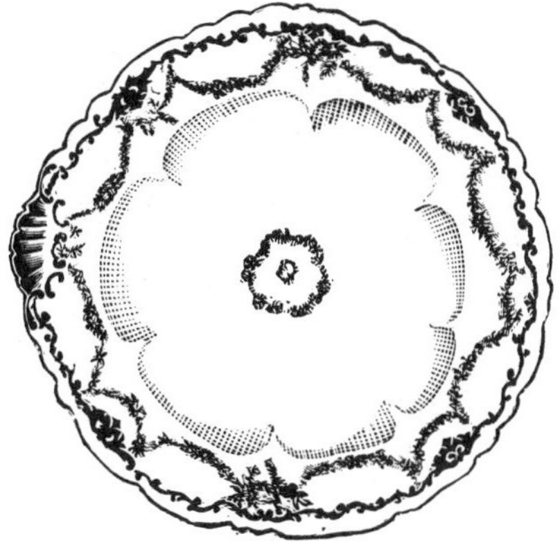

No. 5204

No. 089—Limoges China

Oyster Plate

Border decoration of pink, yellow and blue flowers in festoons; also scroll work on edge in green; clouded gold on handles. This plate is made deep, intended for serving oysters in the half shell on cracked ice. 9½ inches across.

Per dozen $6 60

For Actual Colors see Colored Insert A, following page 78

No. 8151—Limoges China

Oyster Plate

White and gold; fancy lace gold border, and fancy rosette center. Made deep for serving oysters on the half shell.

Medium size 8½ inches per doz., $14 40

Small size, 7½ inches per doz., 13 00

No. 5205

No. 5206

No. 952—Limoges China

Oyster Plate

Cream body from edge extending about 2½ inches toward the center of the plate, with fancy lace border in maroon and green, gold lace border around center of plate and fancy gold rosette center, gold edges.

Large size 9½ inches per dozen, $24 00

Medium size 8½ inches per dozen, 21 90

Small size, 7½ inches per dozen, 19 80

For Actual Colors see Colored Insert G, following page 164

No. 205-0896—Weimar China

Oyster Plate

Cream body, with stippled gold edge and stippled gold around places for oysters.

Per dozen $9 20

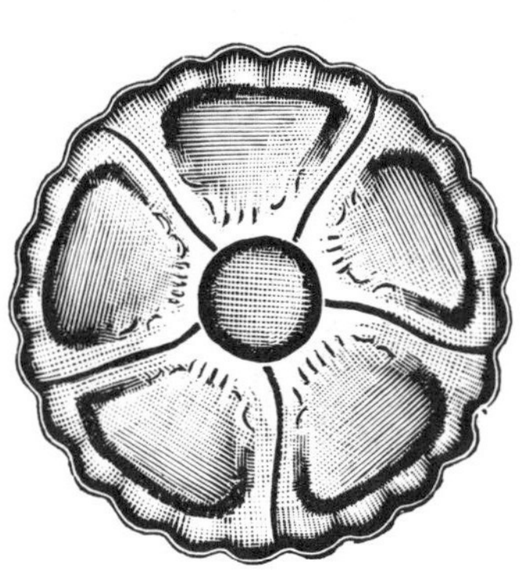

No. 5207

OYSTER PLATES—Continued

No. 5208

No. 4956—Limoges China

Oyster Plate. "Eliza"

Seaweed decoration in combination of gold and green, the gold being decorated over the green, making a charming effect. Heavy burnished gold edges and center.

Per dozen $17 25

No. 8873—Limoges China

Oyster Plate. "Eliza"

Brown seaweed decoration, with clouded gold edges and center.

Per doz $13 80

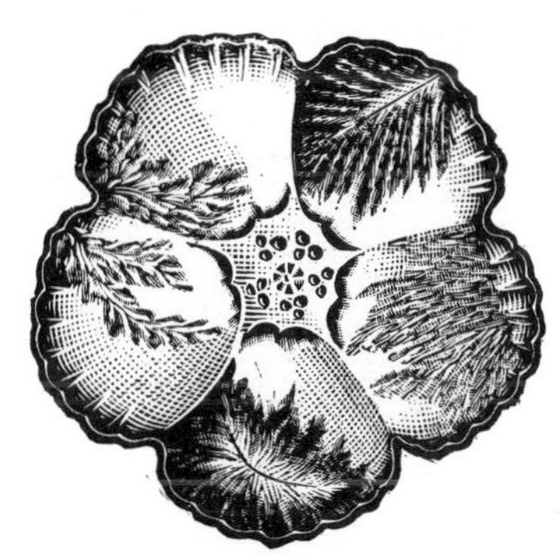

No. 5209

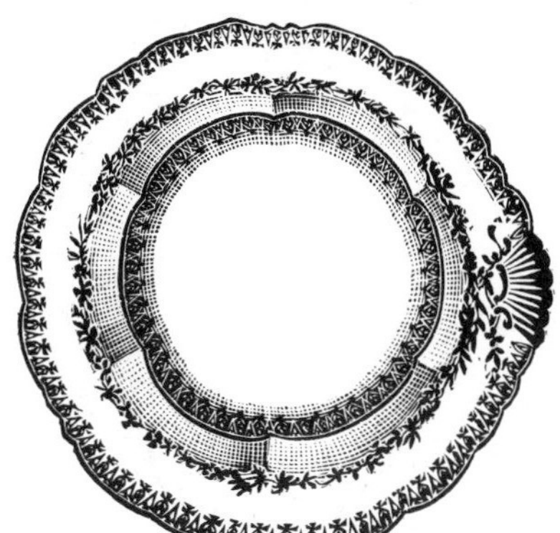

No. 5210

No. 8831

Oyster Plate

Finest Limoges China

Plate made deep for serving oysters on the half-shell. Border decoration of flowers in blue and yellow, rich green leaves, fancy gold lace on edge and inside.

8 inches . per doz. $16 80
7½ " . " 15 15

Oyster Plate

Weimar China

With delicate tints around place for oyster. Gold edge and gold-lined center.

Per doz $4 00

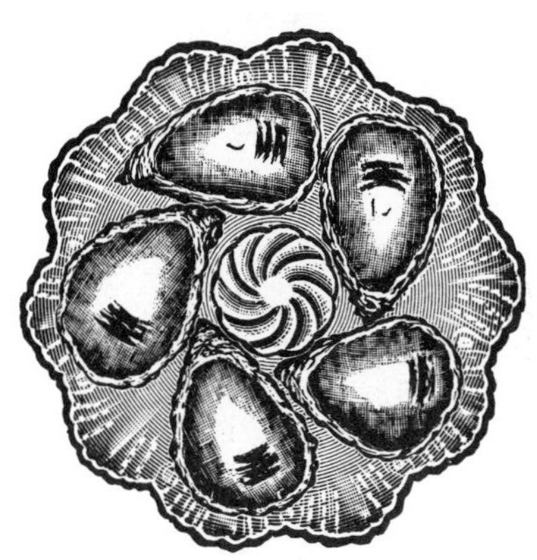

No. 5211

BOUILLON CUPS, TEA CUPS

No. 5212

Bouillon Cup and Saucer

No. 2033—Limoges China

Border decoration of either maroon, green or pink, with gold lace over color, gold foot and edge, fine gold lace border inside; gold traced.

Per dozen................$33 00

No. 5213

Bouillon Cup and Saucer

Austrian China. Border decoration in either maroon, green or yellow; foot also the same color; gold lace work over color and gold lace on edge. Panel decoration of court beauties inside.

Per dozen................$24 00

No. 5214

Bouillon Cup and Saucer

No. 462—Limoges China

Border in either maroon, green or pink, with scattered flower decoration on saucer and inside and outside of cup, gold on foot and gold traced handles.

Per dozen................$13 50

No. 5215

Bouillon Cup and Saucer

No. 472—Limoges China

Festoon of forget-me-nots in blue, with green leaves on inside and scattered flowers on outside, clouded gold on edge, gold traced handles.

Per dozen................$9 00

No. 5216

Cups and Saucers

No. 4948—Finest Limoges China "Perle"

Rococo decoration in sage green, with flowers in pink and light green.

Tea Cups and Saucers, clouded gold handles............dozen $3 60

Tea Cups and Saucers, clouded burnished gold edges and handles..................dozen 5 00

Bouillon Cups and Saucers, clouded gold handles....dozen 1 80

Bouillon Cups and Saucers, clouded burnished handles and edges . ...dozen 6 25

No. 5217

Cups and Saucers

Finest "Elite" Limoges China. Rose decoration in clusters of pink and yellow roses, green leaves.

Tea Cups and Saucers, clouded gold handles............dozen $3 60

Tea Cups and Saucers, clouded gold edges and handles..dozen 5 00

Bouillon Cups and Saucers, clouded gold handles.....dozen 4 80

Bouillon Cups and Saucers, clouded gold edges and handles dozen.......................... 6 25

No. 5218

Cups and Saucers

Finest "Elite" Limoges China "Perle"

Border of green leaves with delicate small pink flowers.

Tea Cups and Saucers, clouded gold handles............dozen $3 60

Tea Cups and Saucers, clouded gold edges and handles..dozen 5 00

Bouillon Cups and Saucers, clouded gold handles....dozen 4 80

Bouillon Cups and Saucers, clouded gold edges and handles, dozen.......................... 6 25

No. 5219

Cups and Saucers

Finest "Elite" Limoges China. Border decoration of lavender flowers, green leaves.

Tea Cups and Saucers, clouded gold handles........... dozen $3 60

Tea Cups and Saucers, clouded gold handles and edges..dozen 5 00

Bouillon Cups and Saucers, clouded gold handles....dozen 4 80

Bouillon Cups and Saucers, clouded gold edges and handles, dozen.......................... 6 25

PUNCH BOWLS

No. 5220

Doulton Punch Bowl

Watteau decoration in flown blue, 8 inches high, 14 inches across. Capacity 2 gallons.

Each $5 50

No. 5221

No. 4701—Limoges China

Punch Bowl on Foot

14 inches across, 9 inches high. Capacity about 2 gallons.

Complete $9 90

No. 5222

No. A-0428—**English Doulton Punch Bowl**

Rich dark blue decoration, with gold vine and lace work on foot, gold edge, also clouded gold in decoration; 10 inches high, 14 inches across; capacity, 2 gallons . . . . **each, $10 50**

No. 5223

No. 093-A—**Punch Bowl**

Limoges China, small chrysanthemum decoration. Gold edges. Capacity, 7½ quarts.

Each $4 00

No. 5224

Punch Bowl on Stand

Finest Limoges China; Orchid decoration; 13 in. across, 8½ inches high; capacity about 2 gallons.

Each $13 50

FOR GIFTS

IT is a noticeable feature of this establishment that a large proportion of the goods sold here, both to resident New Yorkers and customers all over the country, are for Gifts. In the first place, the fact has been recognized for centuries that nothing is more appropriate for the expression of affection and esteem than something choice in Glass or China. For weddings and anniversaries their use has become traditional—they are as much a part of the bride's expectations as a wedding ring, or trousseau.

Nothing of real value makes so much of an exhibition for the money as some of our superb China Sets, and they are often chosen not for that reason alone, of course, but because they are both useful and ornamental. Rich cut glass in single pieces, wine, water and chocolate sets in appropriate cases, are much in demand, prices varying from very modest sums to those "exclusively expensive."

FOR GIFTS—Continued

WE also always carry many beautiful articles of a purely ornamental nature—in many instances only one of a kind, and consequently quite impractical to catalogue. Our magnificent Hall Clocks also make very noble Gifts.

Among advantages to be thought of in ordering goods from us for this purpose is the one that they will, in all probability, be something "different" from what is to be had nearer home—there is less danger of duplication; they will, no matter, how low the cost, at least be worthy, for we deal in nothing but wares of real value, and finally, you are buying, at least,

"One Quarter Less Than Elsewhere."

GIFTS

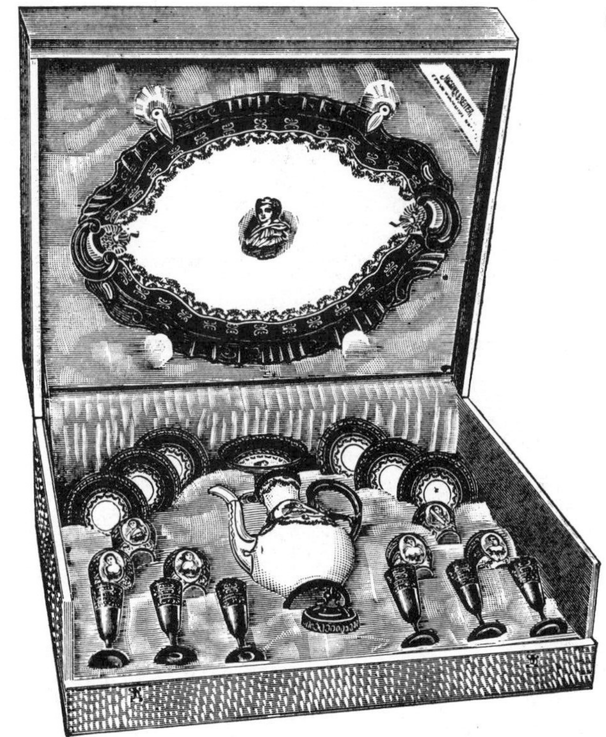

No. 5225

Brandy and Cordial Set

Austrian China, border decoration in either maroon or green, with combination of dark sage green. Panel decoration of celebrated court beauties. Gold lace throughout, and solid gold handles. 1 Tray, 1 Chocolate Jug, 1 Sugar Comport, 6 Cups and Saucers, 6 Cordial Glasses, complete, in white leatherette satin-lined case................$40 35

No. 5226

Chocolate Set

Austrian China, border decoration in either maroon, green or blue, with center decoration of celebrated court beauties. Gold lace throughout, and solid gold handles, 1 Tray, 1 Chocolate Jug, 6 Chocolate Cups and Saucers, complete, in white leatherette satin-lined case..$23 45

GIFTS—Continued

No. 5227

Austrian China Plates

With center figure decoration; border of empire green with fancy gold lace.
12 Plates in case, complete. $10 00
12 Plates only. 6 65

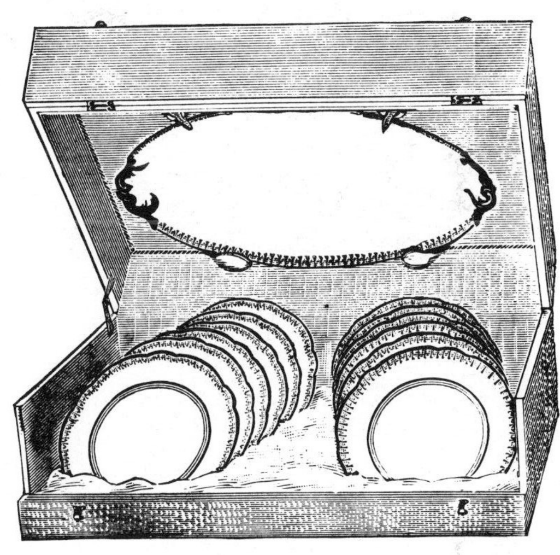

No. 5228

Ice Cream Set

Limoges China, gold lace border, gold line on shoulder of plate, handles of platter solid burnished gold.

12 plates, 1 platter, complete in case............$10 65

GIFTS—Continued

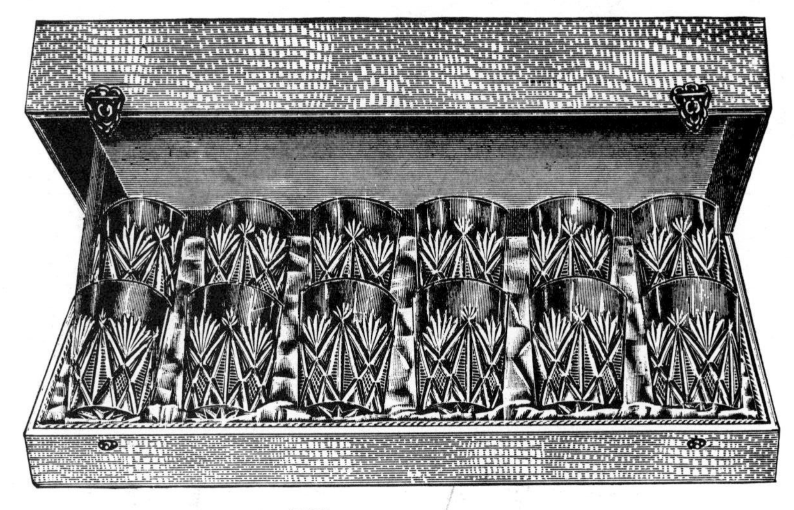

No. 5229

12 Cut Glass Water Tumblers

In satin-lined white leatherette case

Complete $7 25

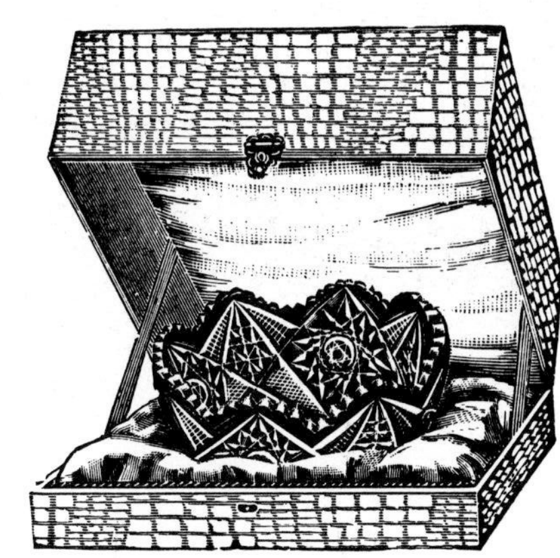

No. 5230

Cut Glass Bowl in Case

Eight-inch Salad, Fruit or Berry Bowl in white satin-lined leatherette case

Complete $5 50

GIFTS—Continued

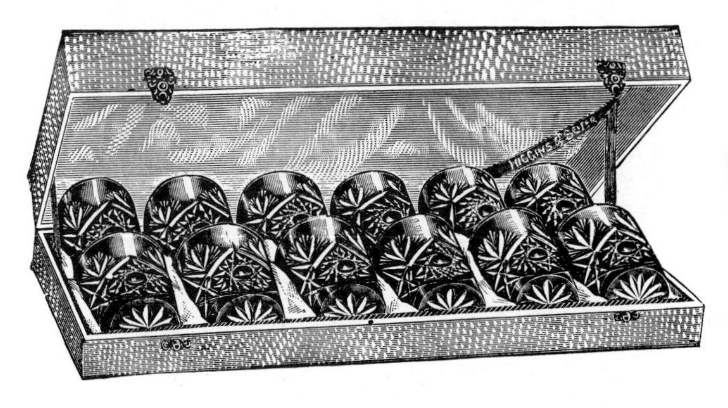

No. 5231

Cut Glass Water Tumblers. "Maple City"

12 cut glass water tumblers in satin-lined, white leatherette case . . . . .complete, $11 75

No. 5232

Cut Glass Water Tumblers

12 richly cut glass water tumblers, "Napoleon." Complete, in satin-lined, white leatherette case $18 50

GIFTS—Continued

No. 5233

Punch Cups or Handled Lemonades in Case

12 cut glass handled punch cups, in satin-lined, white leatherette case . . . . complete, $11 50

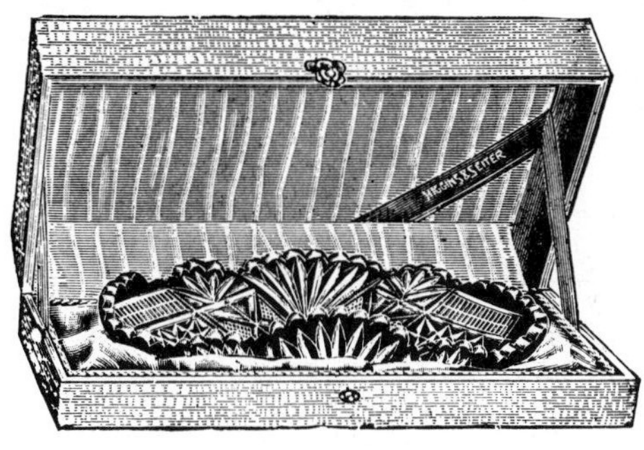

No. 5234

Cut Glass Celery. "Athens"

In white satin-lined leatherette case

Complete $5 00

GIFTS—Continued

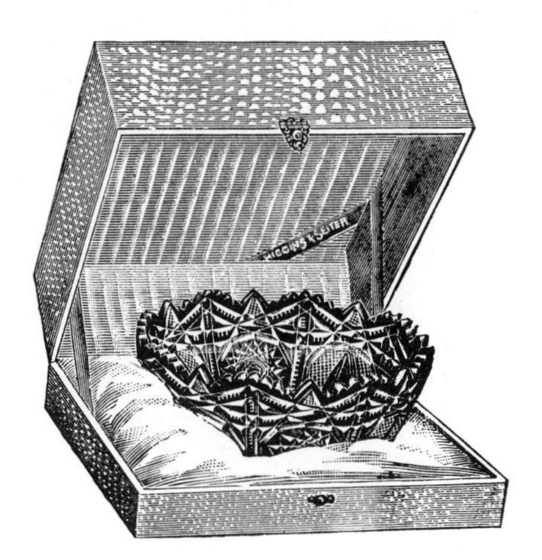

No. 5235

Cut Glass Salad Bowl. "Webster"

10-inch, complete, in white satin lined leatherette case . $16 25

No. 5236

Cut Glass Whiskey Set. "Syrott"

1 Whiskey Jug, 6 glasses, 1 mirror, complete, in satin-lined white leatherette case $19 50

GIFTS—Continued

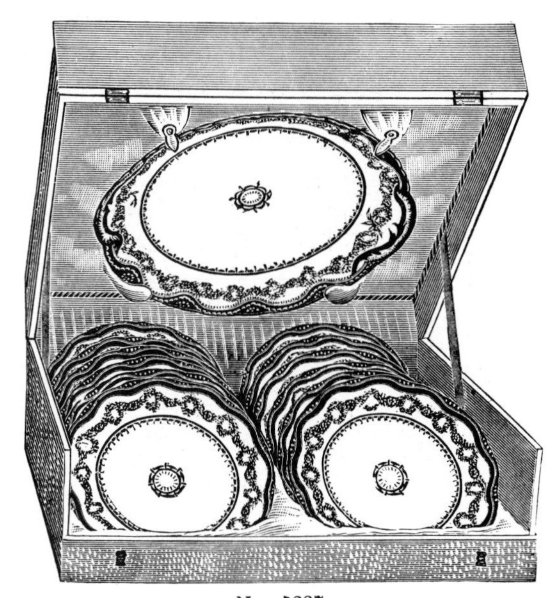

No. 5237

Chop Set

Haviland's Limoges China, border of underglazed Cobalt blue and gold, with hanging festoons of flowers in pink and blue, sage green leaves. Fancy gold on shoulder of plate and fancy gold center.

12 plates, 1 chop platter, complete, in case . . . $37 95

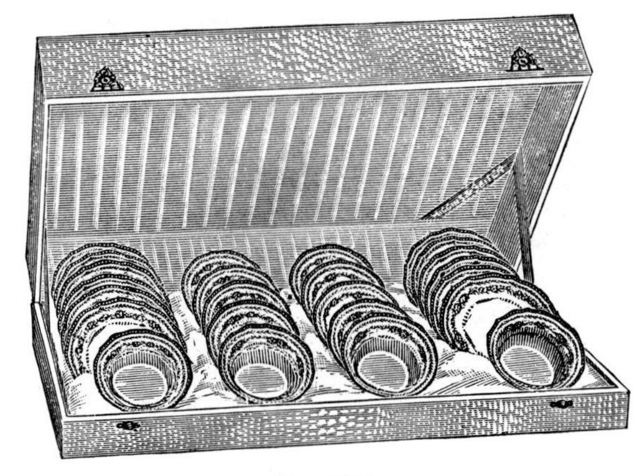

No. 5238

Ramikins and Plates

Elite Limoges China, solid gold beaded border with oak leaves in gold and wreath of flowers in pink, yellow and blue, connecting leaves in green.

12 ramikins and plates, in case $11 60

GIFTS—Continued

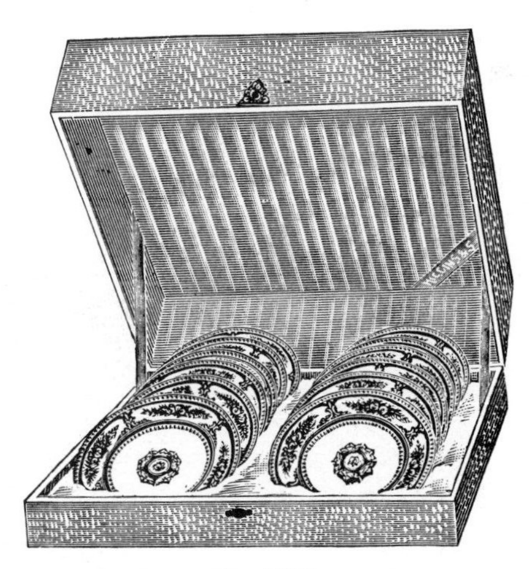

No. 5239

Bread and Butter Plates

Wedgwood English China. Panel border decoration of flowers in pink, blue and yellow, with green and gold leaves, fancy gold edge, fancy center.

12 Plates, with case, complete $16 80
6 Plates, with case, complete 8 90

For Actual Colors see Colored Insert F, following Page 154

No. 5240

Bread and Butter Plates

"Elite" Limoges China. Border decoration in bunches of lavender and yellow flowers, connected with sage green leaves. A lustre border edge and line on shoulder, with gold lace work over the lustre effect. Also shoulder line of flowers, with spray of flowers in center.

12 Bread and Butter Plates in case, complete . . $9 15
6 Bread and Butter Plates in case, complete . . 5 30

For Actual Colors see Colored Insert D, following Page 122

GIFTS—Continued

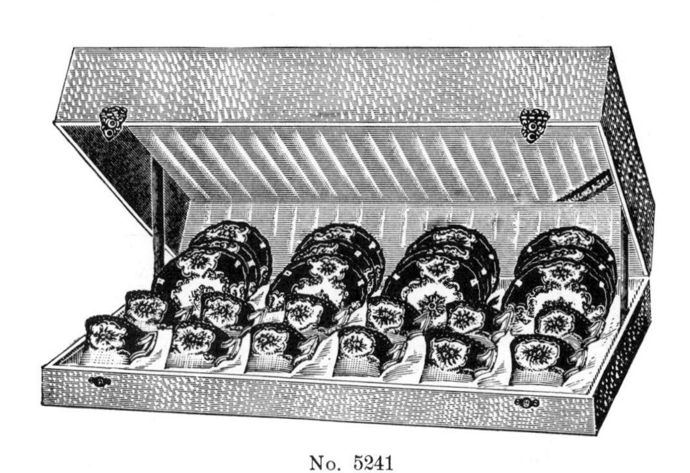

No. 5241

A. D. Cups and Saucers

English Coalport China. Panel decoration of underglazed Cobalt blue, alternating with sprays of flowers in pink and yellow with green leaves; gold spray inside the cup; solid gold edge, gold traced handles.

12 A. D. Cups in case $42 00
6 A. D. Cups in case 21 35

No. 5242

A. D. Cups and Saucers

Haviland's Limoges China. Festoons of flowers in pink and blue, with sage green leaves; stippled gold on edge, stippled gold handles.

12 A. D. Cups and Saucers in case, complete. . . $9 10
6 A. D. Cups and Saucers in case 4 80

CORNERS IN ART ROOM

PLATEAU AND HANDLED MIRRORS

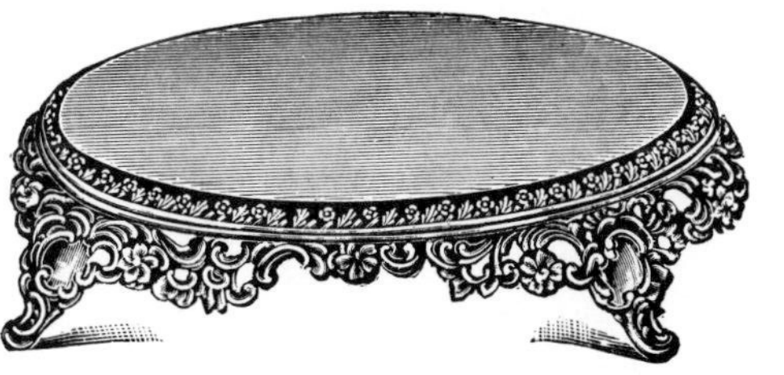

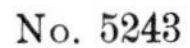

No. 5243

Plateau

Mounting in either gold or silver finish

Size		Price
8-inch	each,	$2 00
10 "	"	2 65
12 "	"	3 25
14 "	"	4 20
16 "	"	5 10
18 "	"	5 45

No. 5245

No. 025—**Handled Mirror Plateau**

Either silver or gold finish

Size		Price
10-inch	each,	$2 20
12 "	"	2 70
14 "	"	3 25
16 "	"	3 90
18 "	"	4 65

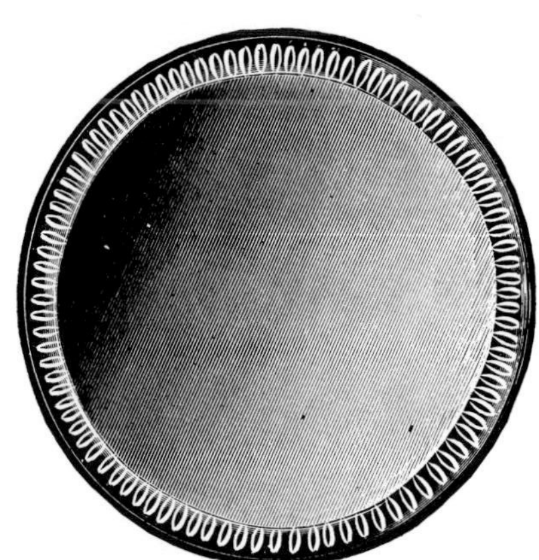

No. 5244—**Mirror Plateau**

Cut beaded border

Size		Price	Size		Price
6-inch	each,	$0 60	14-inch	each,	$1 85
8 "	"	90	16 "	"	2 15
10 "	"	1 20	18 "	"	2 75
12 "	"	1 60			

FIREPROOF PUDDING DISHES

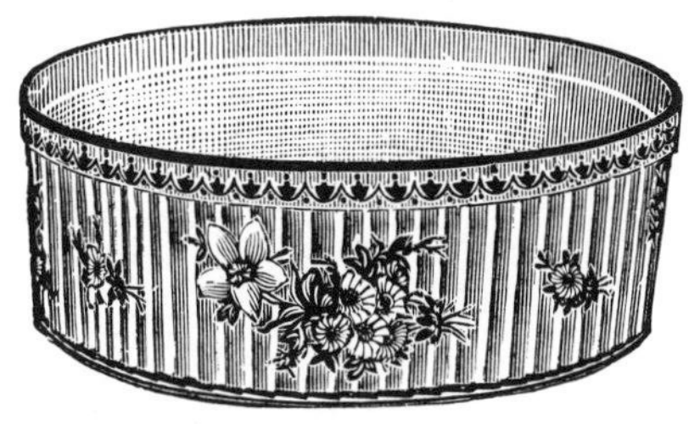

No. 5246

Pudding Dish

Fireproof. Hand painted Dresden flowers. Fancy gold edge,

7¾ inches in diameter . . . . each, $3 40
7 " " " . . . . " 2 90

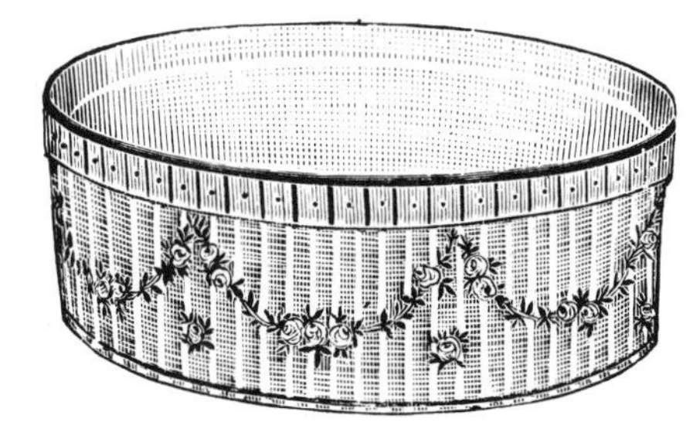

No. 5248

Pudding Dish

Fireproof China. Hand-painted garlands and festoon of roses. Fancy gold edge.

7¾ inches in diameter . . . . each, $3 40
7 " " " . . . . " 2 90

No. 5247

Pudding Dish

Fireproof China. Hand-painted violets and green leaves in natural color. Fancy gold edge.

7¼ inches in diameter . . . . each, $3 40
7 " " " . . . . " 2 90

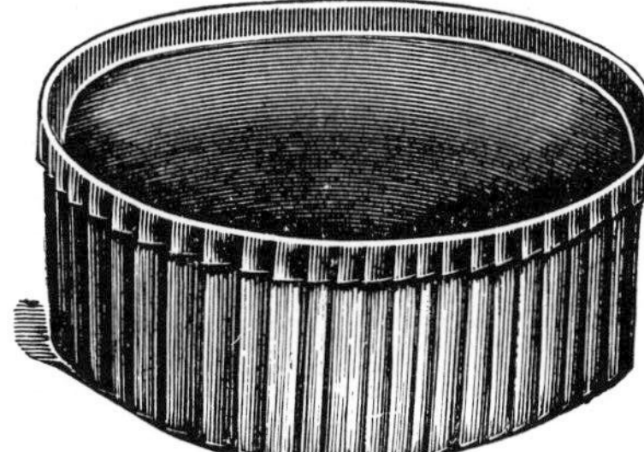

No. 5249

Pudding Dish

WHITE		PINK, YELLOW OR BLUE	
7¾ inches diam., each,	$1 05	7¾ inches diam., each,	$1 25
7 " " "	80	7 " " "	1 05

Ramikin

White, large, 3¼ inches across . . . . per doz., $2 05
White, small, 2¾ " " . . . . " 1 65
Tinted pink or yellow, large . . . . . " 2 50
Tinted pink or yellow, small . . . . . " 2 05

BAKING DISHES, RAMIKINS AND FLOWER VASES

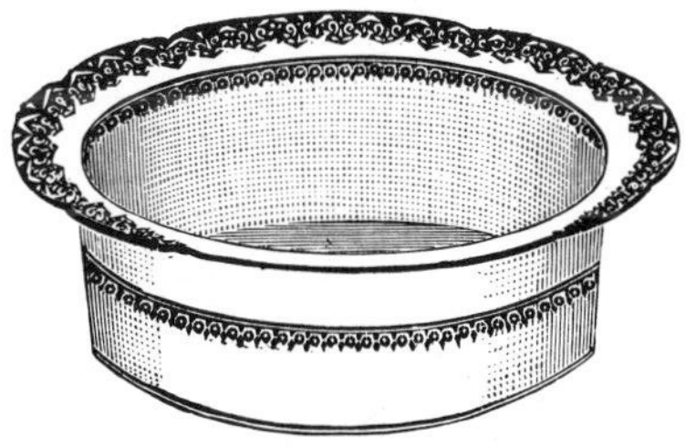

No. 5250

No. 952—Souffle or Baking Dish

Finest Limoges China, with cream border and background, with fancy lace pattern in sage green and red. Fancy gold star rosette center and edges. Small size, 8½ inches from outside to outside edge . . . . price, $3 15

Large size, 10 inches from outside to outside edge, " 3 95

For Actual Colors see Colored Insert G, following page 164

No. 5251

No. 279—Souffle or Baking Dish

Finest Limoges China, used for pudding, macaroni, etc. Border decoration in festoons and garlands of delicate pink yellow and blue flowers with green leaves. Sage green and rococo border. Rosette center with blossoms. Small size, 8¾ inches from outside to outside edge . . . . . . price, $1 00

Large size, 10 inches from outside to outside edge, " 1 35

For Actual Colors see Colored Insert A, following page 78

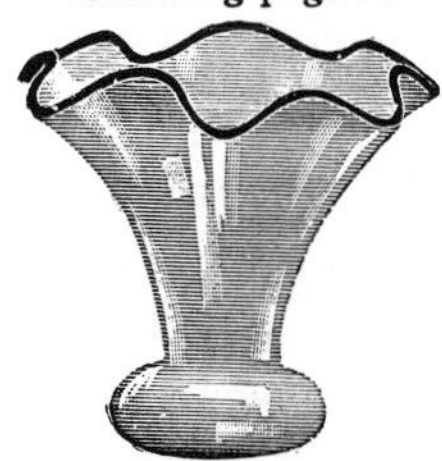

No. 5252

No. 5012—Flower Vase

Iridescent glass, gold edge,	4½ in. high,	$1 25
" " " "	5½ "	1 75
" " " "	6½ "	2 70
" " " "	7½ "	3 85

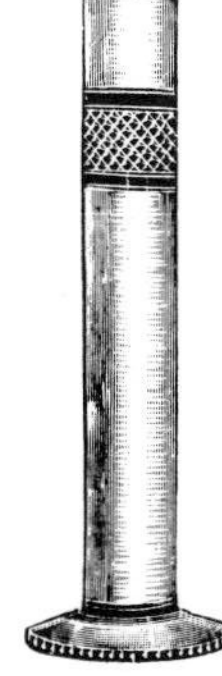

No. 5253

No. 9491—Bohemian Vase

With band of strawberry diamond cutting, with gold band on each side of cutting, and gold edge on foot.

4 inches high .	$0 25	10 inches high .	$0 75
6 " " .	35	12 " " .	1 00
8 " " .	50	14 " " .	1 30

16 inches high $1 85

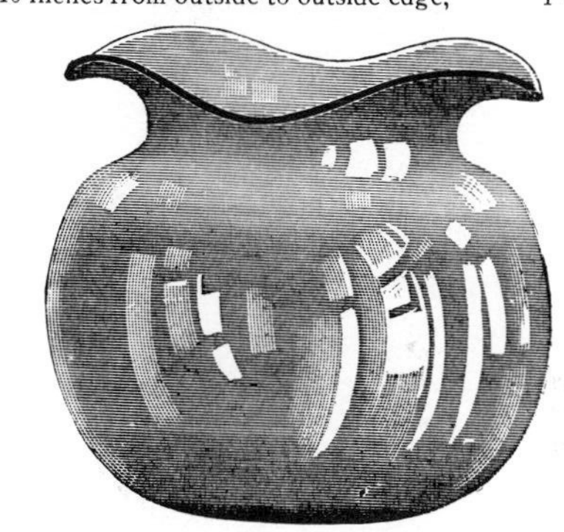

No. 5254

Flower Vase or Rose Bowl

Amber Iridescent glass,	4 inches high.	$1 00
" " "	5½ " "	1 25
" " "	6½ " "	1 60
" " "	8 " "	2 25

RAMIKINS

No. 5255

No. 2524–3213—Ramikin and Pl at

Finest "Elite" Limoges China, border decoration of delicate flowers of pink, yellow and green leaves and a gold border on each side of holly. Edge also heavy burnished gold, 3½-inch opening. Plate, 4½ inches across,

Per dozen $9 60

For Actual Colors see Colored Insert C, following page 100

No. 5258

No. 279—Ramikin and Plate

Limoges China, border decoration in festoons of flowers in pink, yellow and blue, with rococo edge and sage green leaves; also flower decoration in bottom of ramikin. Saucer, 5½ inches across; ramikin, 4 inches.

Per dozen $6 25

For Actual Colors see Colored Insert A, following page 78

No. 5256

Haviland China Ramikin and Plate

Border and center decoration in very delicate pink, green and yellow flowers, gold lace edge. Plate, 5 inches across: ramikin, 3¾ inches.

Per dozen pairs $9 00

No. 5259

Ramikin and Plate

Wedgwood China. Solid colors in either Cobalt blue, red or green; burnished gold lace work over color. Saucer, 5 inches; ramikin, 3⅞ inches,

Per dozen $25 20

No. 5257

Haviland China Ramikin and Plate

Decorated in delicate green and yellow flowers, with clouded gold edge. Plate, 5 inches across, ramikin, 3¾ inches.

Per dozen pairs $5 00

No. 5260

No. 2682—Ramikin and Plate

Haviland China. Border and center decoration of small sprays of flowers with bowknots. Clouded gold edges. Ramikin saucer, 4⅞ inches; ramikin 3¾ inches.

Per dozen $12 00

For Actual Colors see Colored Insert D, following page 122

PUNCH BOWL. TOBACCO JARS

No. 5261

No. 96.—Tobacco Jar. Flemish

Embossed design. Coloring of green, black, brown and ivory. 8 inches high, 4-inch opening,

Each.........................$1 25

No. 5262

No. 644.—Punch Bowl. Flemish

Raised figure and flower decoration in ivory background, in either rich green or red. Height, 9½ inches, 15 inches across, capacity, 2½ gallons.

Each.......................................$5 65

No. 5263

No. 344.—Tobacco Jar. Flemish

Hunting and drinking scenes in raised figure decoration with background in rich browns, greens, reds, etc. Cover has opening for sponge. Height, 12 inches.

Each.........................$1 65

MAJOLICA ASH AND CIGAR TRAYS

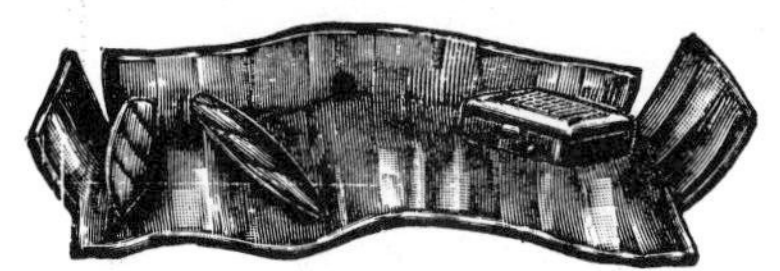

No. 5264

No. 2088-7.—Ash and Cigar Tray

Cigar and Match Safe shown in exact reproduction. Size, 7½ x 6 inches.

Each $1 10

No. 5265

Ash Receiver

Imitation of iron weight, showing reproduction of matches. 5 inches across.

Each.................$0 45

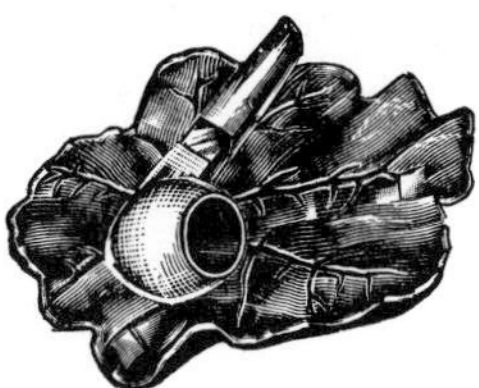

No. 5266

No. 1671—Ash Tray

Showing reproduction of pipe. 5¼ inches across.

Each $0 25

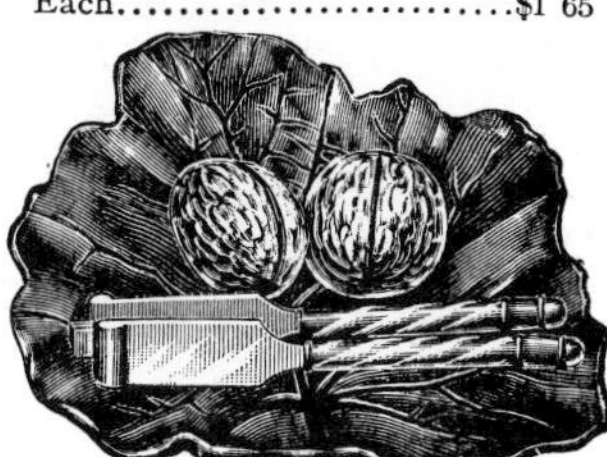

No. 5267

No. 2671.—Ash Tray

Showing reproduction of nuts with nut crackers. 6 inches across.

Each..........................$0 30

PLAQUES

No. 5268

Plaque

Revolutionary Series. Washington and Lafayette at Valley Forge

Delft blue; border of small stars. 15 inches across.

Each $5 00

No. 5269

Plaque

Revolutionary Series. Spirit of '76—Yankee Doodle

Delft blue; with border of small stars. 15 inches across

Each $5 00

PLAQUES—Continued

No. 5270

Italian Cantagalli Plaque

Center has figure decoration with figure, etc., as border decoration in combined tints throughout of yellow, blue and green, with dark scroll work. We cannot guarantee the decoration of these plaques to always be the same, although they will always be of the same general character.

11¾ inches	$5 00	20 inches	$18 00
16 "	9 00	24 "	27 00

No. 5271

Plaque

English Cauldon, assorted, blue Delft decorations

14¾ inches across

Each $1 50

BEER SETS

For General Effect and Coloring of Steins
see Colored Insert H, following
page 206

No. 5272

No. 14—**Flemish Beer Set**

Ivory background, raised figures, with dark green, red and brown coloring throughout.

1 large Stein, 6 small steins and 1 wooden tray, set complete $9 75

No. 5273

No. 073—**Flemish Beer Set**

Ivory background, with leaves, vines, etc., in dark green and brown figures in relief.

1 large stein, 6 small steins, and 1 wooden tray, set complete $7 75

STEINS

For General Effect and Coloring of Steins see Colored Insert H, following page 206

No. 5274

No. 97—Flemish Stein

Ivory background with raised embossed figures, with delicate colorings of brown, green and maroon. 20½ inches high $7.80

No. 5275

No. 85—Flemish Stein

Background in delicate tints of black and green, with raised ivory figures, representing "War." 15½ inches high.................. $5.60

No. 5276

No. 553—Flemish Stein

Figures in ivory effect. Background dark green, brown, and some of the parts in blue.

Height, 17½ inches, ...	$4.40
" 22 "	5.95

STEINS—Continued

For General Effect and Coloring of Steins see Colored Insert H, following page 206

No. 5277

No. 0443—**Mettlach Stein**

Raised figure design in ivory, with background of light blue. Brown and light blue decoration on foot. 7½ inches high.

Each, ... $2.60

No. 5278

No. 3902—**Mettlach Stein**

Playing card design. Figures in brown; card design in red. Background in gray. 6 inches high.

Each, . . . $2.40

No. 5279

No. 25—**Flemish Stein**

Embossed effect in ivory, with background of brown, green and purple.

Height, 13½ inches.

Each, ... $2.00

No. 5280

No. 1722—**Mettlach Stein**

Drinking scene. Combined colors of green, pink, yellow and steel gray. German motto. 8½ inches high.

Each, ... $1.85

STEINS—Continued

For General Effect and Coloring of Steins see Colored Insert H, following page 206

No. 5281

No. 2042.—**Mettlach Stein**

Figure decoration in tapestry effect. Combined tints in brown, blue, gray and gold. Bottom of sage green. 9 inches high.

Each $3 25

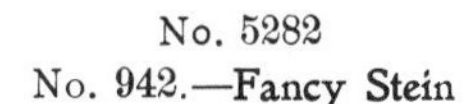

No. 5282

No. 942.—**Fancy Stein**

Figure decoration in bas-relief, green background, figures in ivory. Height, 16½ inches.

Each $2 65

No. 5283

No. 054.—**Fancy Stein**

Raised figure decoration in ivory, with background of dark reds and greens, harmoniously tinted throughout. Height, 14 inches.

Each $3 00

STEINS—Continued

For General Effect and Coloring of Steins see Colored Insert H, following page 206

No. 5284

No. 674.—**Flemish Stein**

Figures in high colors. Border decoration in the tints of purple, green and black.

10½ inches high

Each $1 35

No. 5285

No. 654.—**Flemish Stein**

Background in brown and green. Figures in raised ivory color. German motto.

11 inches high

Each $1 35

No. 5286

No. 04.—**Flemish Stein**

Ivory body and raised ivory figures. Border in sage green and black. German inscription.

11 inches high

Each $1 35

No. 5287

No. 7422.—**Mettlach Stein**

Blue background, **with** raised figures in ivory. Wedgwood design.

6¾ inches high

Each **$1 25**

STEINS—Continued

For General Effect and Coloring of Steins see Colored Insert H, following page 206

No. 5288

No. 474—Flemish Stein

Background in brown, raised figures in ivory. German inscription.

8¼ inches high

Each $1 00

No. 5289

Flemish Stein

Ivory background with figures in relief, size to top of handle.

5½ inches high

Price . . . . . each, $0 60

No. 5290

No. 612—Flemish Stein

Background of brown, with green border on top and motto.

7½ inches high

Each $0 85

No. 5291

No. 012—Pokal or Mug

Ivory Background, figures in brown and green and black.

6½ inches high

Price . . . . . . each, $0 50

CUSPIDORS AND JUG

No. 5292

No. 984—**Flemish Cuspidor**

Ivory background, relief work in dark green and brown.

10 inches high

Each $2 25

No. 5293

No. 084—**Flemish Cuspidor**

Ivory background, figures in relief, panels of dark green and brown.

9½ inches high

Each $1 90

No. 5294

Flemish Jug

Ivory background and ivory effect, with green and brown decoration throughout, height 11 inches, capacity about 2½ quarts.

Each $2 25

TOBACCO BOXES AND ASH RECEIVERS

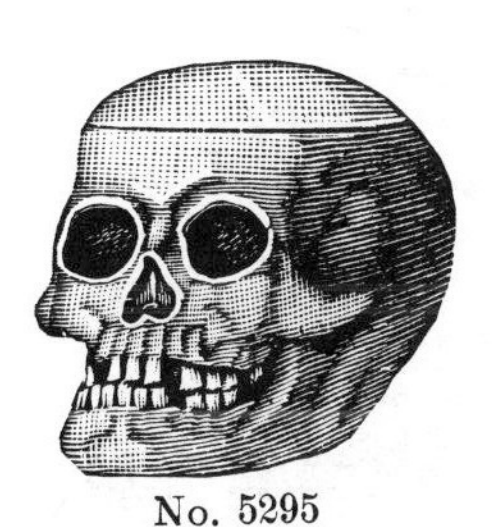
No. 5295

No. 5296

No. 5297

No. 5298

TOBACCO BOXES

Head designs. Hats lifting off, making receptacle for tobacco inside. Choice of any design.
Each, ... $0.25

No. 5299

No. 5300

No. 5301

No. 5302

FROG ASH RECEIVERS

After models of Old Dresden. Frogs in natural colors. Choice of any design.
Each, ... $0.45

No. 5303

No. 9261—Roman Punch or Sherbet Cups

Saucer 5 inches across. Cup 2⅝ inches high.
Per dozen,..................................$18 00

No. 5306

No. 5005—Handled Bon Bon or Olive

4½ inches across,............................ $1 25

No. 5309

No. 6812—Handled Bon Bon or Olive Dish

7 inches extreme measure,..............each, $2 35

GOLD GLASS

The design is first cut in the glass and then filled in with best burnished gold; edge gold also.

No. 5304

No. 0605—Salad, Fruit or Berry Bowl

6 inches,................each, $3 00
7 " .... " 4 25
8 " .... " 5 75

No. 5307

No. 7362—Compotier

5 inches,...................... $2 35
6 " 4 25

No. 5310

No. 6502—Salted Almond Dish

5 inches extreme measure. 2 inches high.
Each,........................$1 35

No. 5305

No. 9035—Roman Punch or Sherbet Cups Footed

Saucer 5 in. across. Cup 2⅞ in. high.
Per dozen,.................................. $24 00

No. 5308

No. 2505—Footed Bon Bon or Fruit Dish

4 inch,.. $1 25
5 " 1 60
6 " 2 35
7 " 3 25

No. 5311

No. 7605—Fruit, Berry or Bon Bon Dish

6 inch,.. $3 85
8 " 6 25

OLIVE DISHES AND BOHEMIAN GLASS VASES

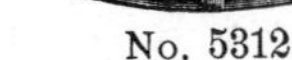

No. 5312

No. 7741—**Bohemian Glass Vase**

Ocean green, heavily decorated with raised gold and gold edge.

10½ inches high	each	$2 25
13½ " "	"	2 75
15½ " "	"	4 15
19½ " "	"	6 40
23½ " "	"	11 25

No. 5313

No. 0505—**Olive, Pickle or Bon Bon**

Each $1 60

No. 5314

No. 0222—**Footed Olive or Bon Bon**

4 inches across $1 00

No. 5315

No. 381-3685—**Bohemian Glass Vase**

Ocean green glass with violets and roses in enamel. Solid burnished gold extending from top of vase down about 3½ inches, gold line on foot, also around base.

8 inches high	each	$1 75
10 " "	"	2 50
12 " "	"	3 50
14 " "	"	4 50
16 " "	"	5 50

No. 5316

Fruit, Salad or Berry Bowls

Decoration of cut flowers and cut edge filled in with best burnished gold.

No. 9168.	6 inches	each	$3 75
"	7 "	"	4 50
"	8 "	"	5 65
"	9 "	"	6 75

No. 5317

Comport, Cut and Gold

The flowers are first cut in the glass and then filled in with burnished gold.

No. 6475, 5 inches across, 2½ inches high . . . . . each, $2 40

FAIRY LAMPS, CANDLESTICKS, FLOWER VASES, Etc.

No 5318

No. 6003-782—**Fairy Lamp**

Bohemian glass, with artificial leaves on stem. 8¼ inches high.

Price, including 1 taper . each $0 25

Extra tapers. . . . . . . dozen 25

No. 5319

Glass Flower Vases

Made to represent an open lily. The glass is the opalescent effect, combining the tints of pink, yellow, green, etc.

4 inches high . . . . . . each $0 75

5 " " . . . . . . " 1 25

7 " " . . . . . . " 2 00

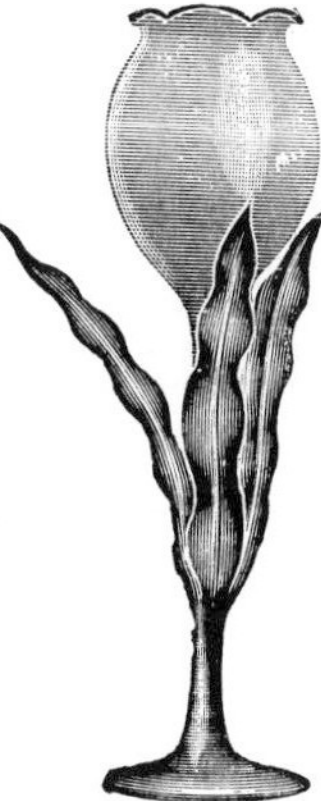

No. 5320

No. 6043-262—**Fairy Lamp**

Bohemian glass with artificial leaves on stem.

8¼ inches high.

Price, including 1 taper . . each $0 25

Extra tapers, doz. 25

No. 5321

Candlestick. "Wedgwood"

Blue body, raised white figure.

8½ in. high . each $2 24

No. 5322

Candlestick. "Wedgwood"

Handled

Blue Body, raised white figure

5 inches . . . . each $1 65

No. 5323

Glass Candlestick

Twisted, 9 inches high . . each $0 25

CANDLE SHADES

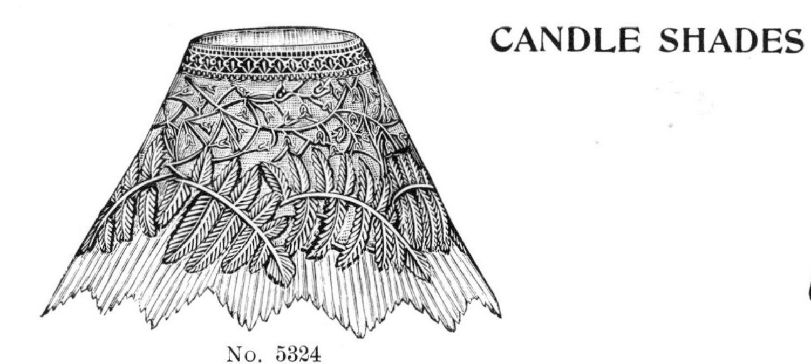

No. 5324

No. 306--Paper. Pink, yellow, green, red, white, and gold, and white and silver

Each $0 10

No. 5325

No. 19--Linen. Pink, yellow, green or red

Each $0 38

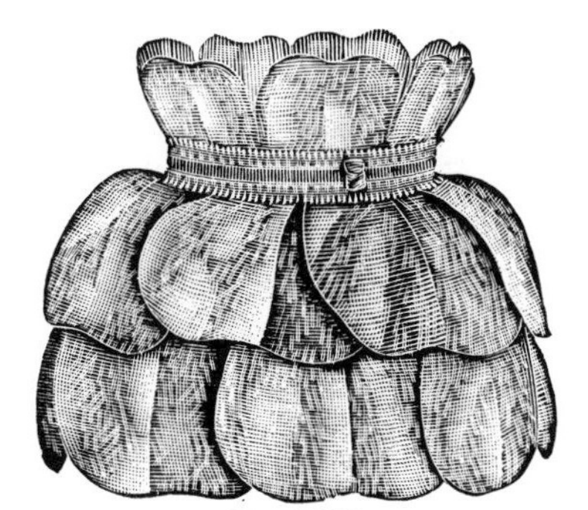

No. 5326

No. 48--Linen outside and paper lining. Pink, yellow, green and red

Each $0 38

No. 5327

No. 49—Silk outside and paper lining. Pink, yellow, green and red

Each $0 75

CANDLES

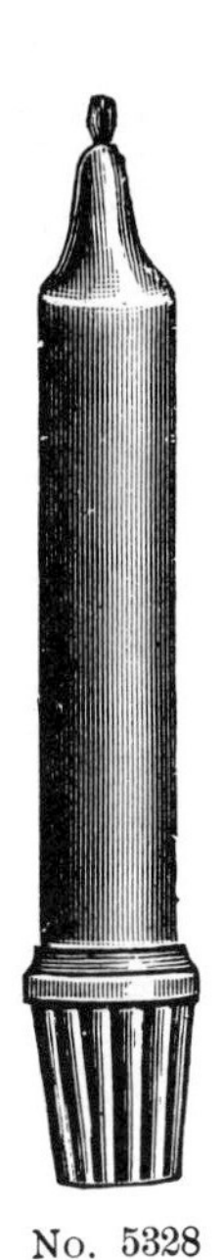

No. 5328

Plain

8 colors: blue, red, orange, white, yellow, pink, green and maroon.
Each $0 05

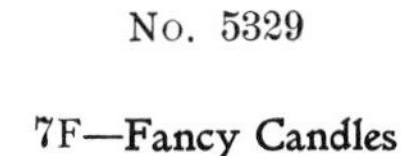

No. 5329

7F—Fancy Candles

6-inch; raised gold vine, pink, yellow, green, lavender, red, white.
Each $0 10

No. 5330

Fancy Candles
No. 52

5-inch; raised gold vine; pink, yellow, green, lavender, red, white.
Each $0 12

No. 5331

Fancy Candles
No. 62

5-inch; fleur-de-lis in raised gold; pink, yellow, green, lavender, red, white.
Each $0 12

No. 5332

Fancy Candles
No. 81

5-inch; small dots in raised gold; pink, yellow, green, lavender, red, white.
Each $0 17

BOBECHES, SHADE HOLDERS, FIXTURES, Etc.

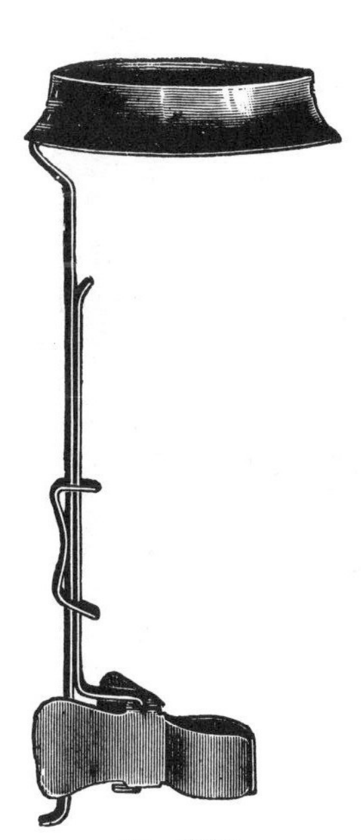

No. 5333

Shade Holder

Brass . . . . each, $0 05

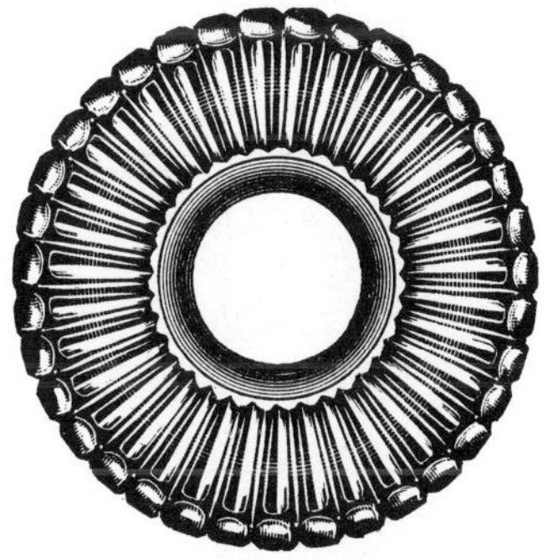

No. 5334

Bobéche. Pressed Glass

Each $0 05

No. 5335

Bobéche. "Gold Star"

Each $0 10

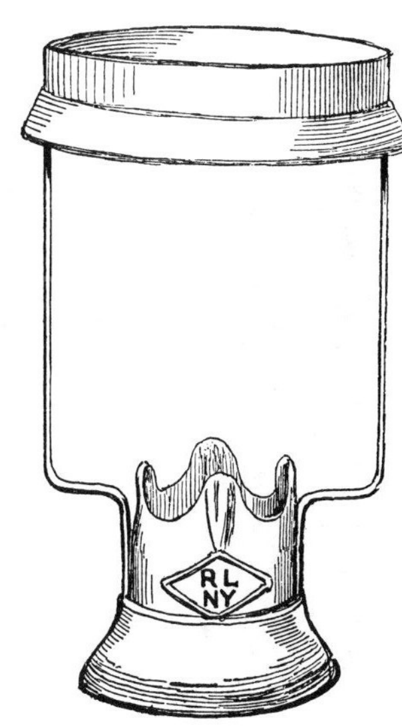

No. 5336

Shade Holder

Self-adjusting (sliding down as the candle burns)

Brass . . . . each, $0 10

Silver . . . . " 15

JARDINIERE AND PEDESTAL

No. 5337

No. 2741.—Jardiniere

Decorated with pansies in natural colors with sage green leaves. Gold traced throughout, and clouded gold top and handles.
11 inches across . . . . each, $4 00

No. 5338

Jardiniere and Pedestal

Mottled Rookwood effect in warm browns and yellows. Jardiniere 10 inches across, height of two pieces complete, 27½ inches.
Jardiniere and Pedestal, complete, $7 00
Sold separately,
Jardiniere $2 50
Pedestal 4 50

No. 5339

No. 945.—Flower Pot

Underglaze in delicate tints of yellow and brown, Rookwood effect.

7-inch	$ 40
8- "	75
9- "	1 00
10- "	1 50
11- "	2 25
12- "	3 00

JARDINIERE AND PEDESTAL—Continued

No. 5340

Jardiniere and Pedestal

No. 615.—Blue, light brown, red or green.

Jardiniere has 9-inch opening, 26 inches high.

2 pieces, complete, $5 00

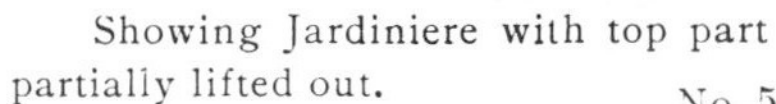

Showing Jardiniere with top part partially lifted out.

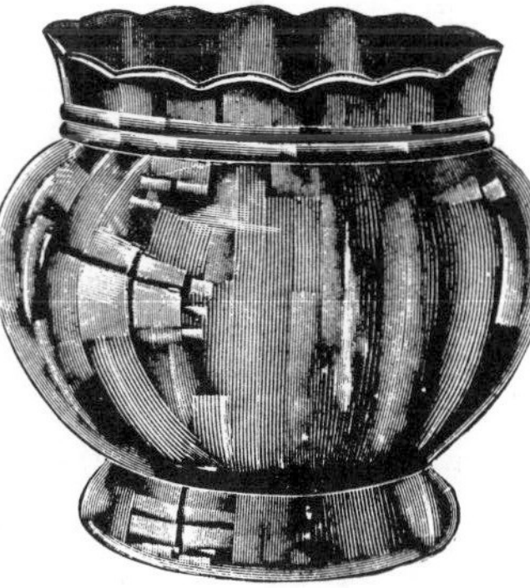

Showing Jardiniere in use.

No. 5341

Jardiniere

In Rookwood effect in warm browns, in 2 pieces. Top can be lifted out for planting or cleaning.

6-inch	each,	$1 00
7 "	"	1 40
8 "	"	2 10
9 "	"	3 00

No. 5342

Jardiniere and Pedestal

"Dolphin"

Dark brown at bottom with blue at top. Jardiniere has 12½ inch opening; 31 inches high.

2 pieces, complete . $10 00

TEAKWOOD PEDESTALS

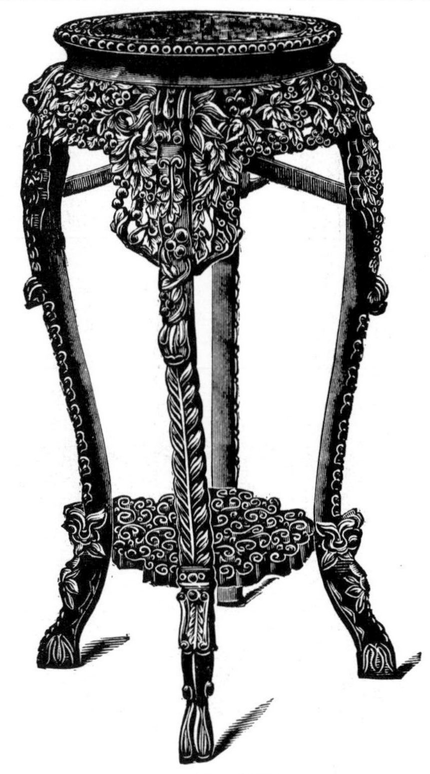

No. 5343

No. 097—**Teakwood Pedestal**

Richly hand-carved throughout with grapes and leaves; inlaid marble top. 16 inches across top, 36 inches high; black or red wood. Each $37 50

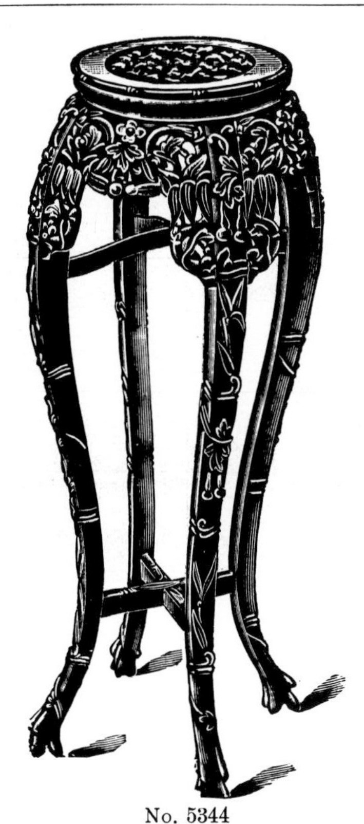

No. 5344

Teakwood Pedestal

Hand-carved; marble top; 36 inches high; 11 inches across the top.

Each $16 50

TEAKWOOD PEDESTALS—Continued

No. 5345

No. 267—**Teakwood Pedestal**

Shelf underneath ; richly hand carved throughout; black or red wood. 17 inches across, 26 inches high.

Each $21 25

No. 5346

Teakwood Pedestal

Hand-carved, marble top. 18 inches high, 17½ inches across.

Each $16 50

TEAKWOOD PEDESTALS

(Continued)

No. 5347

No. 48 D—**Teakwood Pedestal**

Hand-carved; 10½ inches across, 19 inches high. Marble top; black or red wood.

Each $8 50

UMBRELLA JARS

No. 5348

No. 194—**Flemish Umbrella Stand**

Ivory background, with design in dark green and brown; height 25½ inches.

Prices $7 90

No. 5349

No. 783—**Flemish Umbrella Jar**

Raised embossed work with dark green background, with center raised figure decorations in ivory and light green. Raised embossed work throughout, relieved in rich colors, 25 inches high, 10½ inches across. Each $7 50

PLATE, CANDLESTICK, MATCH HOLDER, TOBACCO BOX

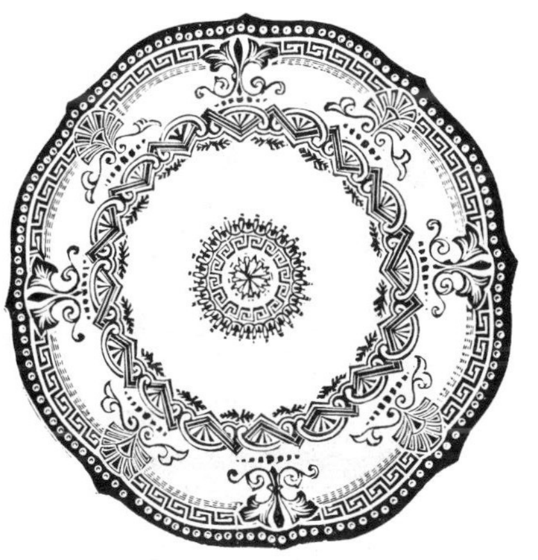

No. 5350

No. 1713-2033—Plate

Finest "Elite" Limoges China. Border decoration extending from edge of plate about 2 inches toward center, in either green, maroon or pink, with fancy colored and gold rosette center; gold decoration also on edge; beaded edge of heavy burnished gold.

PLATES

Dinner, 8½-inch.........	per doz.	$30 00
Soup, 8-inch	"	28 80
Breakfast or Entree, 7½-in.	"	27 00
Tea or Dessert, 6½ inch..	"	21 60
Bread and Butter, 5½ inch	"	15 00

CUPS AND SAUCERS

Tea C. and S., footed.....	per doz.	$31 80
A, D. Coffee C. and S....	"	27 00
Bouillon C. and S........	"	33 00

The following articles can also be had in this decoration.

Chop Dish......................	each	$6 60
Ice Cream Dish...............	"	7 80

No. 5353

No. 81731—Hanging Match Holder

Green border decoration around edges with Dresden flowers in natural colors, traced gold. 2½ inches across, 4½ inches long.

Each...............................$0 25

No. 5351

Rose Candlestick

Made of porcelain, resembling wax. Assorted colors, pink, red or yellow, with green leaves.

Each...............................$0 25

No. 5352

Rabbit Plate

Made—after several years' unsuccessful effort to find in market something in the way of a Welsh rabbit plate that would be a decided novelty, at once unique and inexpensive—from our own suggestions, artistically colored, in six different designs.

Per dozen...........................$4 50

No. 5354

No. 1162—Tobacco Boxes

Spirit Jug design, with pipe.

Each..........$0 75

JUGS

No. 5355

Lincoln Jug

Made of English China, in dark blue, with portrait of Lincoln on both sides, and his famous saying: "With malice toward none, with charity for all."

Size 6,	capacity 2 quarts	$1 75
" 12,	" 3 pints	1 15
" 24,	" 1 quart	85
" 30,	" 1 pint	60

No. 5356

Jug

Copeland Spode Tower, blue decoration.

Size 42,	capacity ¾ pint	each	$0 23
" 36,	" 1 "	"	29
" 30,	" 1¾ pints	"	35
" 24,	" 2½ "	"	40
" 18,	" 3½ "	"	46
" 9,	" 5¾ "	"	80
" 6,	" 4 quarts	"	1 20
" 4,	" 4½ "	"	1 60

For Actual Colors see Colored Insert D, following page 122

No. 5357

Washington Jug

Belleek China. Jug, representing Washington in full Continental uniform; the coat in Continental blue, buttons and handle of sword in burnished gold. Also burnished gold line around base and top of hat.

No. 1,	capacity 5/16 pint	each	$1 00
" 2,	" ⅝ "	"	1 35
" 3,	" 1¼ "	"	1 75
" 4,	" 2¼ pints	"	2 25
" 5	" 3¾ "	"	3 00

WEDGWOOD CHINA. SUGARS AND CREAMERS, ETC.

English Wedgwood. Blue body, with raised white figures.

No. 5358
Jug

Size 36, ½ Pint	each,	$0 95
" 30, 1 "	"	1 05
" 24, 1¼ Pints	"	1 50
" 12, 1½ "	"	1 90
" 6, 2 Quarts	"	3 05

No. 5359
No. 641—**Tea Pot**

Size 42, 2 Cups	each,	$1 30
" 36, 3 "	"	1 50
" 30, 4 "	"	1 85
" 24, 6 "	"	2 10
" 18, 9 "	"	2 70
" 12, 12 "	"	3 05

No. 5360
No, 641—**Sugar Bowl**

Size 30 . . each, $1 55 Size 24 . . each, $1 85

No. 5361
No. 641—**Creamer**

Size 30, ⅓ Pint	each,	$1 00
" 24, ½ "	"	1 35

No. 5262
Tea Pot

Hawthorne Ware. Blue and white decoration.
With Strainer . . . . . each, $0 25

No. 5363
Coffee Biggin

For making dripped coffee. Fireproof China, dark blue Dresden decoration.

Cups,	2	4	6	8	12
Each,	$1 35	$1 90	$2 60	$3 15	$3 75

PÂTE-SUR-PÂTE VASES

These vases are made in Germany, and are a reproduction of the celebrated French Pâte-sur-Pâte vases. The body of the vases is in dark green lustre, with figures in relief on a background of chocolate brown; gold traced handles; gold on foot of vase.

For Actual Colors see Colored Insert H, following page 206

No. 5364
Two-Handled Vase
9½ inches high . . $5 50

No. 5365
No. 8042-4—Vase
8 inches high $4 75

No. 5366
No. 9042-4—Vase
8½ inches high . . . $5 10

No. 5367
Cylinder Shape Vase
Each $3 00

PÂTE-SUR-PÂTE VASES—Continued

For Actual Colors see Colored Insert H, following page 206

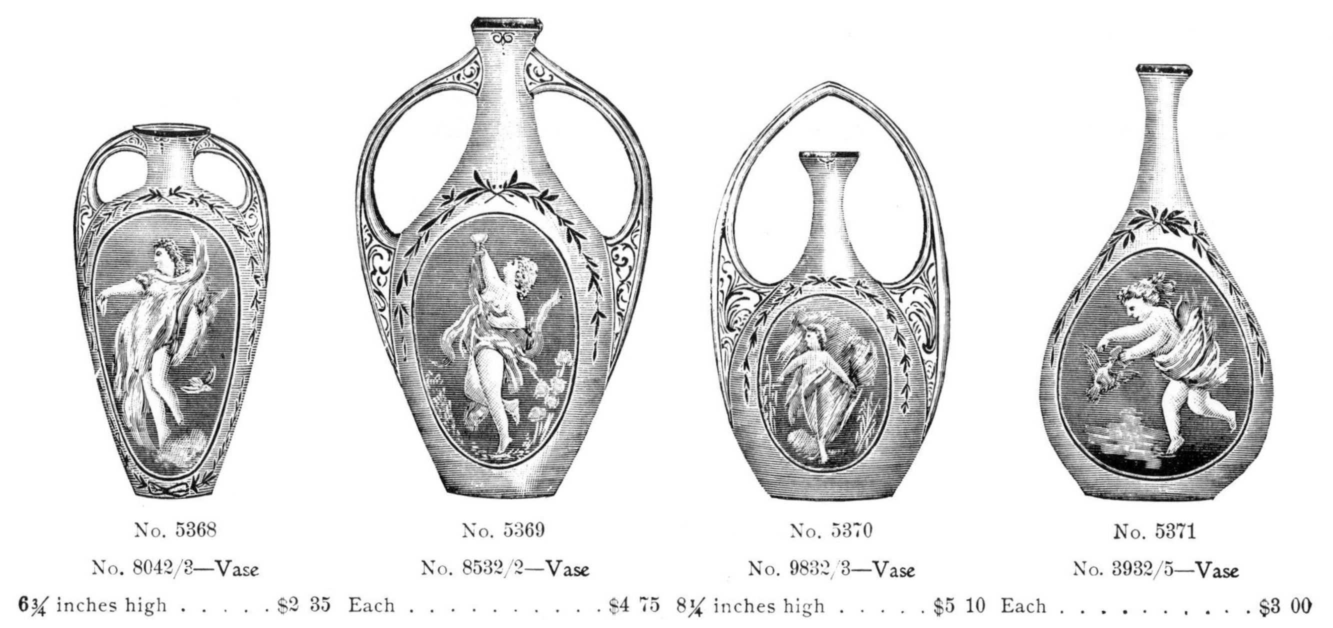

No. 5368	No. 5369	No. 5370	No. 5371
No. 8042/3—Vase	No. 8532/2—Vase	No. 9832/3—Vase	No. 3932/5—Vase
6¾ inches high $2 35	Each $4 75	8¼ inches high $5 10	Each $3 00

INFORMATION FOR ORDERING GOODS, TERMS, Etc.

Be sure to write your name legibly.

Be sure to state distinctly amount of money sent.

Do not mutilate catalogue by cutting out illustrations, as you will be perfectly understood by giving number and page only.

State how you want your goods forwarded ; whether by express or freight.

State if we may substitute in case any selection has been sold.

HOW TO FORWARD MONEY

Remittances should be made by draft, certified check, post office or express money order, payable to Higgins & Seiter, New York City, or, if more convenient, by money or postal note, registered.

TERMS

All orders of $5 or less must be accompanied by remittance in full. Orders amounting to more than $5 can be sent by express C. O. D. and (return money charges), but must be accompanied by a deposit of one-fifth the amount of purchase, which will be deducted from bill accompanying goods.

C. O. D.

Goods cannot be sent on approval, or C. O. D. subject to inspection, as the express companies refuse to accept goods in this manner, and we warrant all goods as represented.

EXCHANGING GOODS

We will exchange any goods that are not satisfactory, providing return charges on goods are prepaid.

SHIPPING GOODS

All purchases will be delivered free within 100 miles of New York City.

On all purchases amounting to not less than $10.00 freight will be prepaid to the nearest railroad station in all of the following States : Maine, New Hampshire, Vermont, Massachusetts, Rhode Island, Connecticut, New York, New Jersey, Pennsylvania, Maryland, Virginia, N. Carolina, S. Carolina, Ohio, Indiana, Michigan, Illinois.

All purchases of $25.00 or over will be fully prepaid to the nearest railroad station in all of the States east of the Mississippi River.

On all orders amounting to not less than $10.00 for points west of the Mississippi River, freight will be prepaid as far west as Chicago, Ill., and St. Louis, Mo.

REFUNDING OF BALANCES

When a balance is due after filling an order, it will be returned at once with a bill of items.

PACKING OF GOODS

We make no charge for packing, and guarantee safe delivery. Any claims should be made at once.

SPECIAL NOTICE

Our mail order department is under the personal supervision of a member of the firm, and orders intrusted to us will receive the same attention as though you were here in person.

SENDING GOODS BY MAIL

Packages which, when packed ready for shipping, do not weigh to exceed 4 pounds, can be sent by mail at the rate of 1 cent per ounce, and can be insured for 5 cents per package.

SATISFACTION GUARANTEED

INDEX

A

D

E

F

G

H

I

J

K

L

M

N

O

P

T

U

V

W

Detach Here and Use This Blank for Ordering

ORDER BLANK

Date ____________________ *190*

Messrs. HIGGINS & SEITER

50, 52 and 54 West 22d Street, New York

Please forward to M ____________________

May we substitute in case any selection has been sold? ______ *Address* ____________________

County ____________________ *State* ____________________

The goods as per list below, for which find enclosed ____________________

and forward via ____________________

(State here whether to ship by express or freight)

No. Page in Cat.	No. Article	Quantity	DESCRIPTION	Price Complete Each or Doz.	TOTAL
			TOTAL		

(OVER)

No. Page in Cat.	No. Article	Quantity	DESCRIPTION	Price Complete Each or Doz.	TOTAL
			AMOUNT FORWARD		
			TOTAL		

ORDER BLANK

Date ____________ *190*

Messrs. HIGGINS & SEITER

50, 52 and 54 West 22d Street, New York

Please forward to M ____________

May we substitute in case any selection has been sold? ______ *Address* ____________

County ____________ *State* ____________

The goods as per list below, for which find enclosed ____________

and forward via ____________

(State here whether to ship by express or freight)

No. Page in Cat.	No. Article	Quantity	DESCRIPTION	Price Complete Each or Doz.	TOTAL
			TOTAL		

(OVER)

No. Page in Cat.	No. Article	Quantity	DESCRIPTION	Price Complete Each or Doz.	TOTAL
			AMOUNT FORWARD		
			TOTAL		

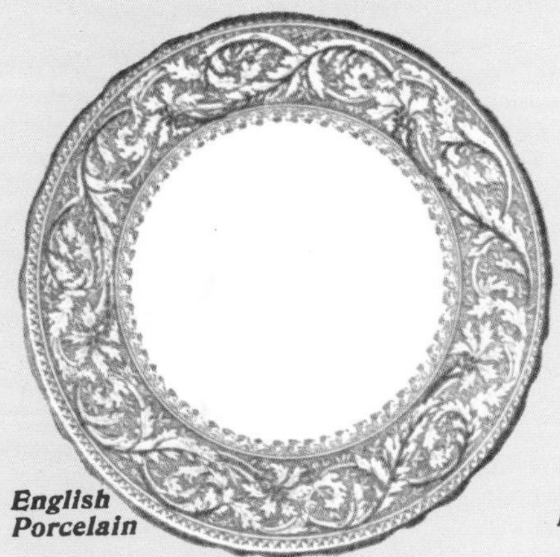

English Porcelain

For description and prices see pages 118, 150.

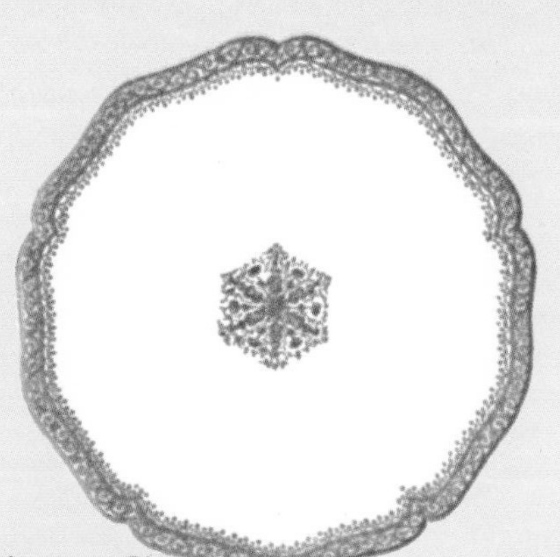

Limoges China

For description and prices see page 81.

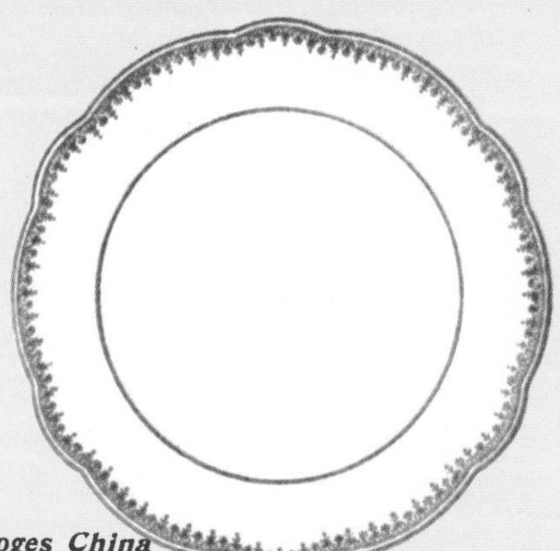

Limoges China

For description and prices see pages 95, 148, 153, 221.

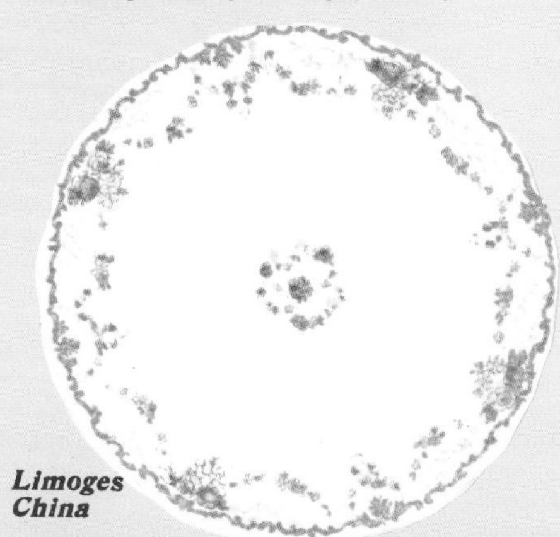

Limoges China

For description and prices see pages 96, 195, 222, 241, 242.

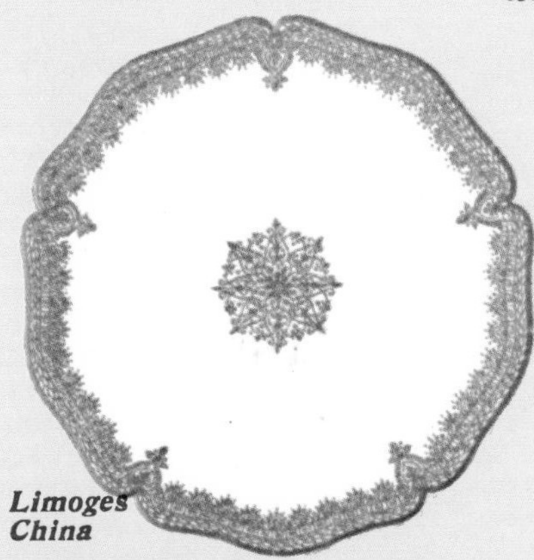

Limoges China

For description and prices see page 85.

Limoges China

For description and prices see page 87.

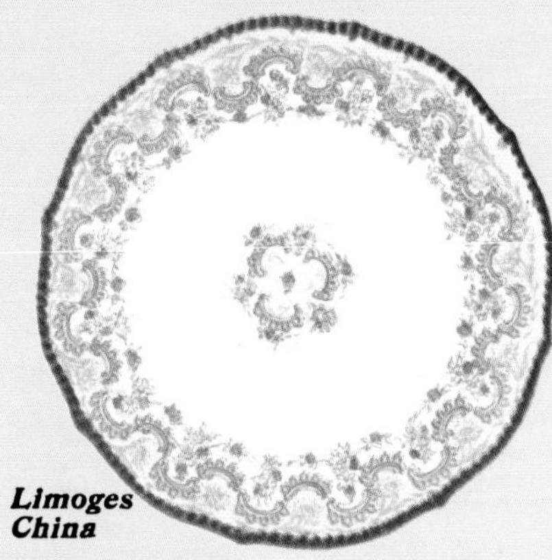

Limoges China

For description and prices see pages 88, 152, 167, 168, 169, 221.

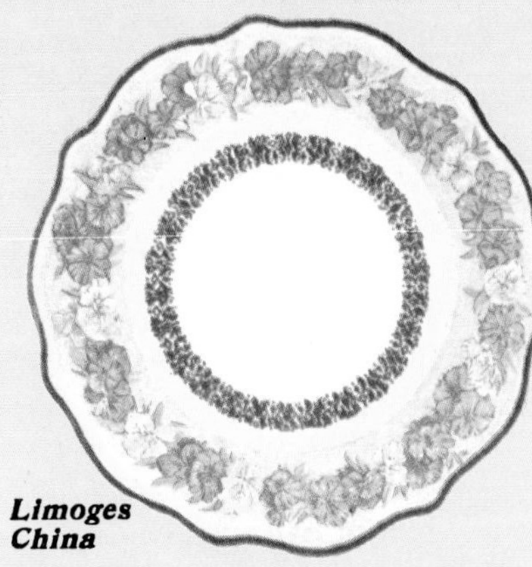

Limoges China

For description and prices see pages 157, 158, 159, 160, 161.

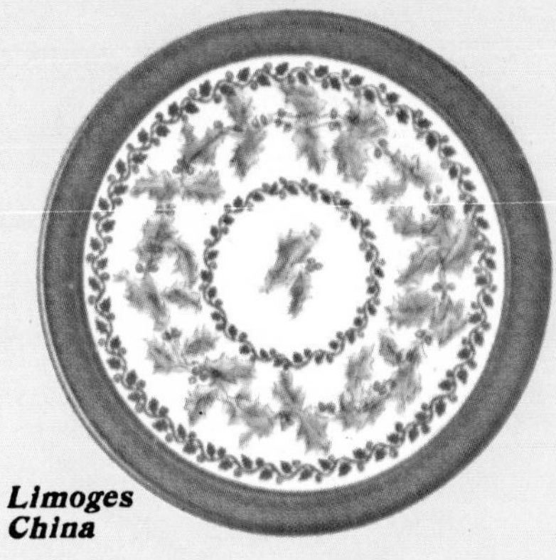

Limoges China

For description and prices see pages 173, 174, 175.

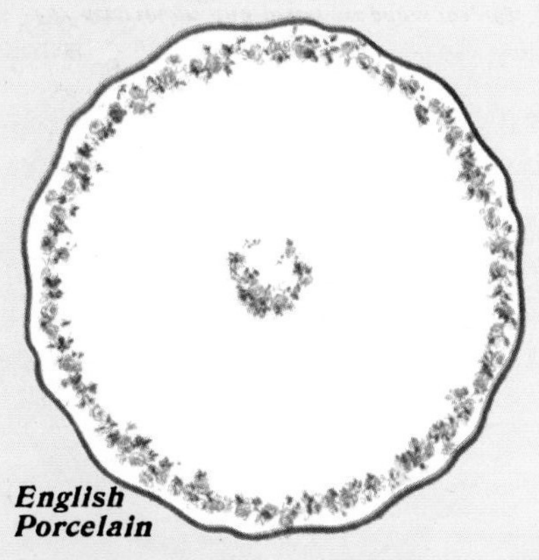

English Porcelain

For description and prices see page 125.

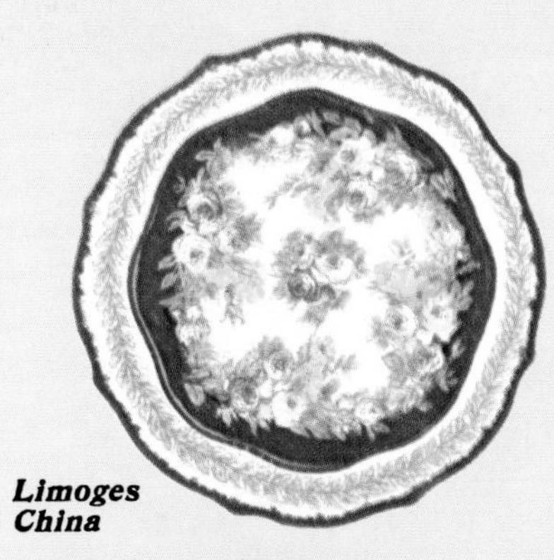

Limoges China

For description and prices see pages 170, 171, 172.

Maddock English Porcelain

For description and prices see pages 116, 153.

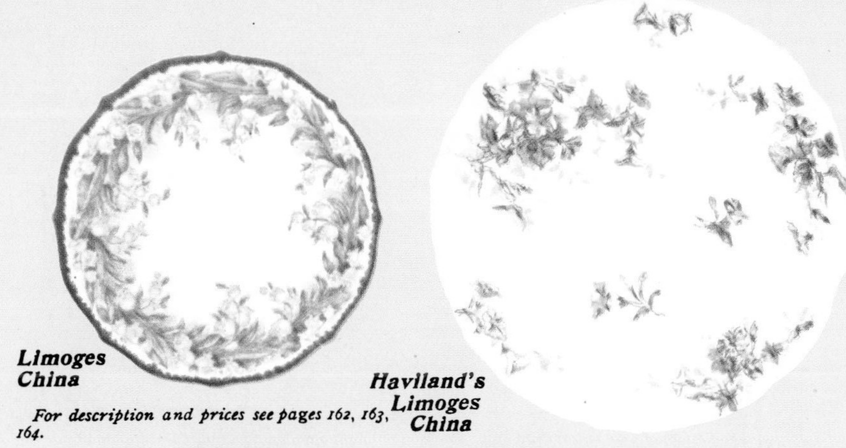

Limoges China

For description and prices see pages 162, 163, 164.

Haviland's Limoges China

For description and prices see pages 100, 154.

Limoges China

For description and prices see pages 190, 191, 192, 193.

Cauldon English China

For description and prices see pages 78, 149.

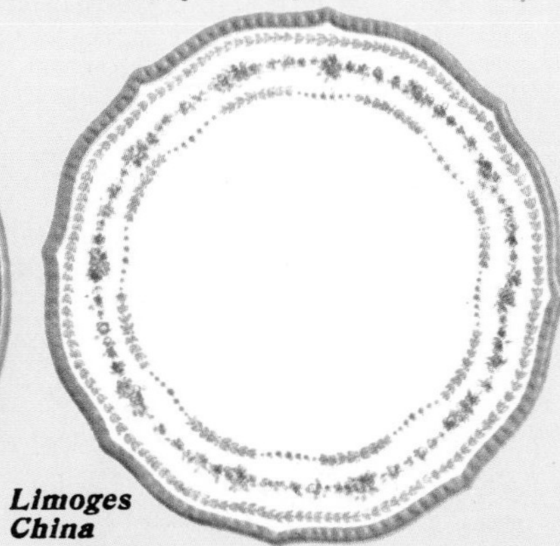

Limoges China

For description and prices see pages 84. 176, 177, 242.

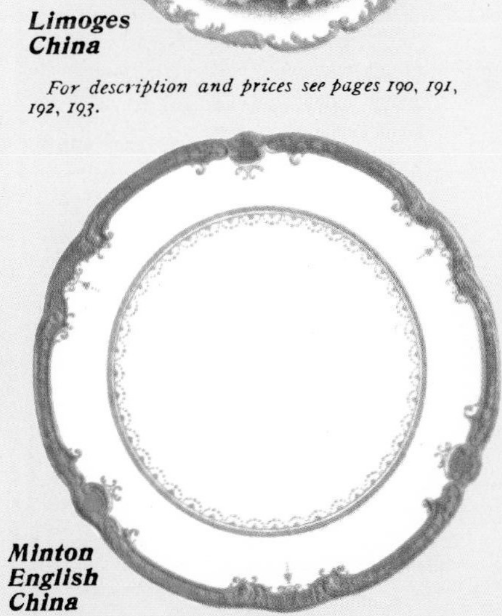

Minton English China

For description and prices see page 100.

Toilet Set

For description and price see page 137.

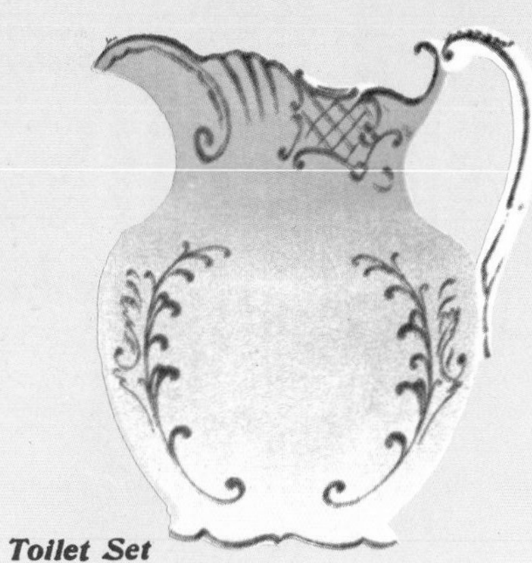

Toilet Set

For description and price see page 135.

Toilet Set

For description and price see page 132.

Toilet Set

For description and price see page 139.

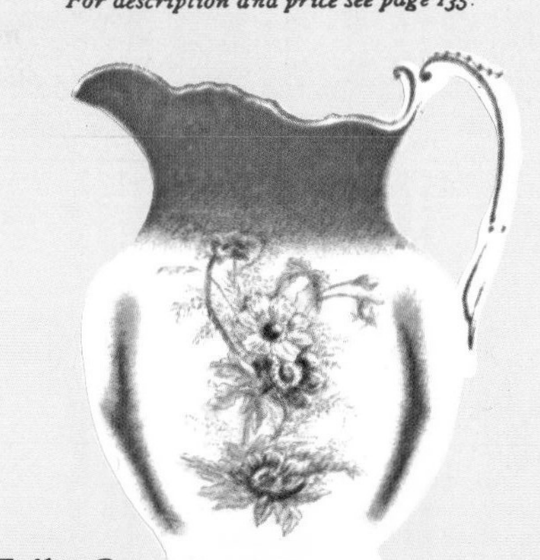

Toilet Set

For description and price see page 137.

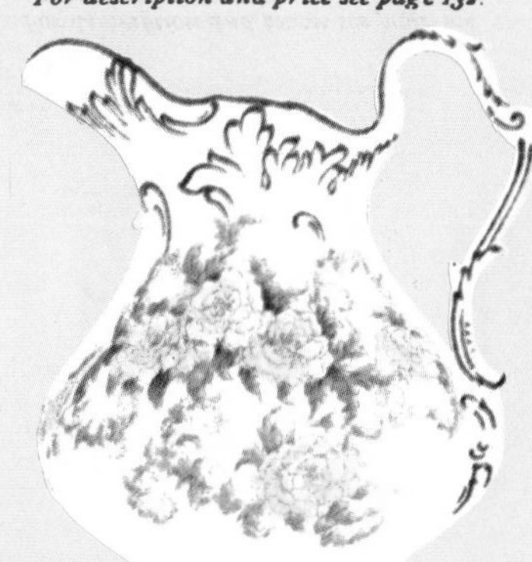

Toilet Set

For description and price see page 132

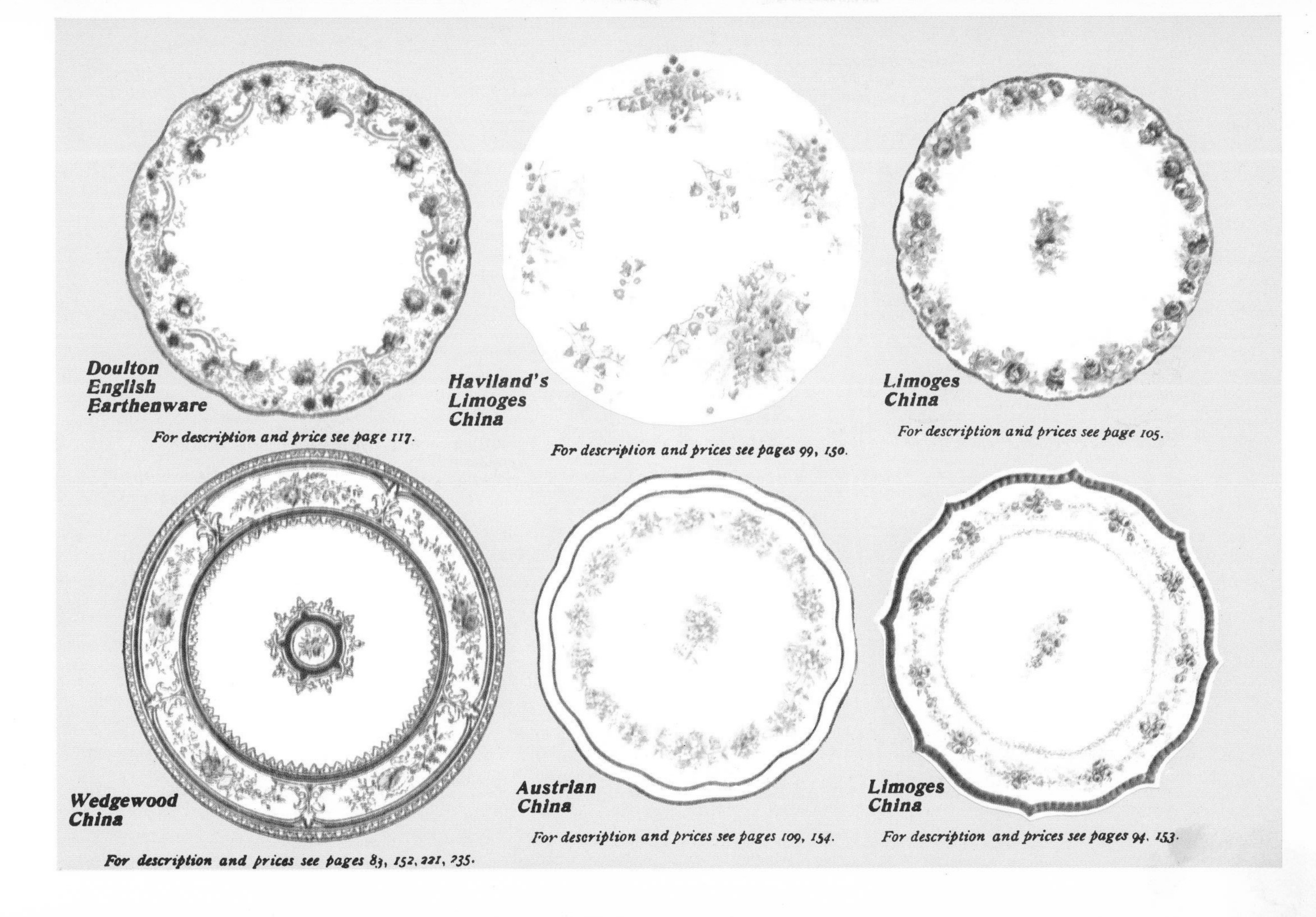

For description and price see page 117.

For description and prices see pages 99, 150.

For description and prices see page 105.

For description and prices see pages 83, 152, 221, 235.

For description and prices see pages 109, 154.

For description and prices see pages 94, 153.

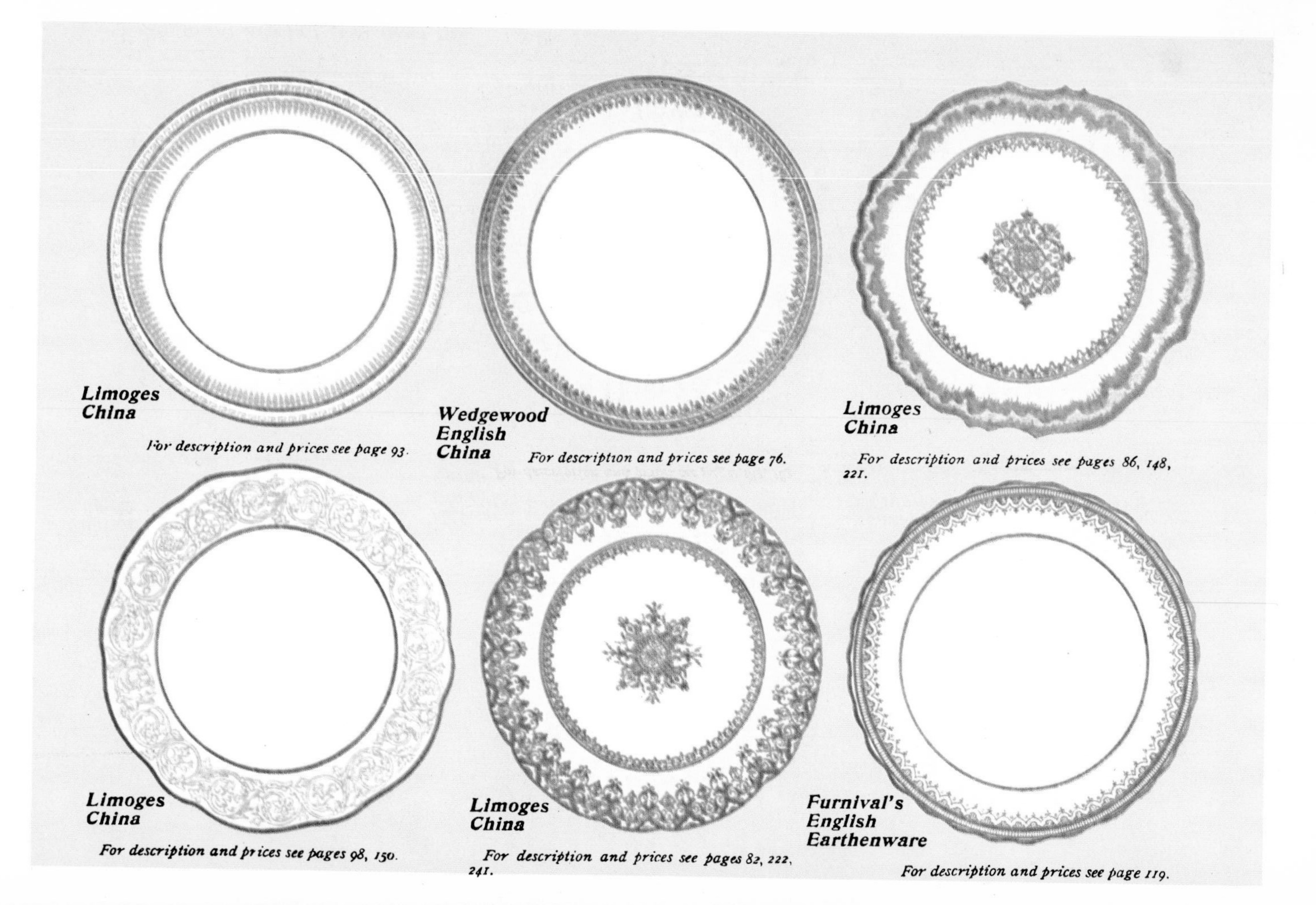

For description and prices see page 93.

For description and prices see page 76.

For description and prices see pages 86, 148, 221.

For description and prices see pages 98, 150.

For description and prices see pages 82, 222, 241.

For description and prices see page 119.

Dresden

For description and prices see pages 198, 199.

Dresden

For description and prices see pages 182, 183.

Dresden

For description and prices see pages 196, 197.

Stein

For description and prices see pages 246, 247, 248, 249, 250, 251.

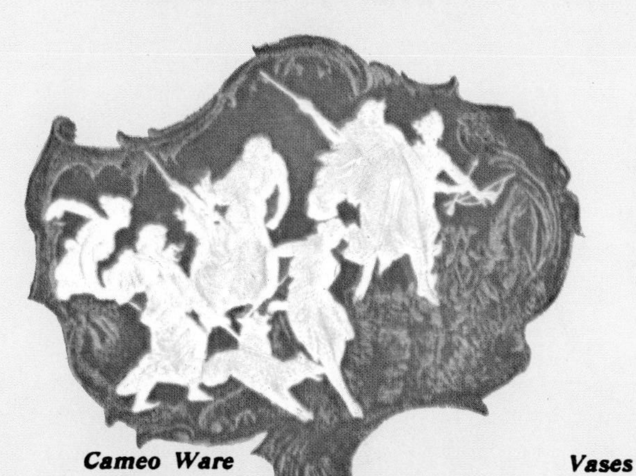

Cameo Ware

For description and prices see pages 215, 216, 217, 218, 219.

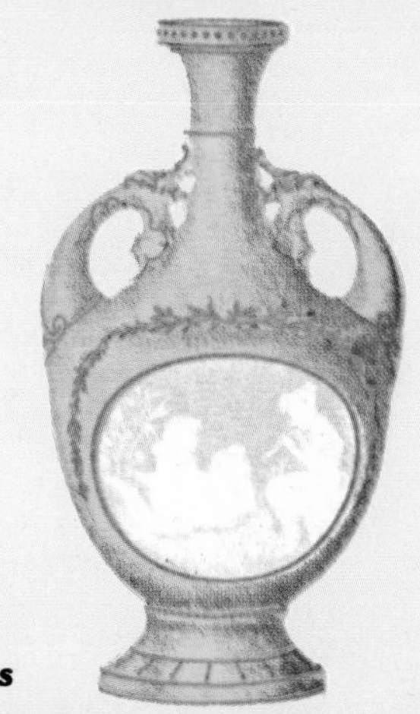

Vases

For description and prices see pages 268, 269.

China and Cut Glass

HIGGINS & SEITER
an historical introduction

"Though the devices by which 'Society' is amused are countless," wrote Mary E. Carter, author of *Millionaire Households,* in 1903, "no function seems to find such lasting favor as the dinner-party . . . most popular of all [being], the large dinner-party numbering twenty-four guests and upward." Miss Carter wrote her book as a guide for professional housekeepers in the baronial establishments that stood in proud array along New York's Fifth Avenue, Newport's Bellevue Avenue, and Chicago's Gold Coast. But the style of life of these great houses, with their ostentatious display of hospitality, was something that middle-class housewives in Maine and Iowa and Colorado wished to emulate.

A formal dinner, at the turn of the century, consisted of several courses requiring an almost bewildering display of glittering crystal, shining silverware and lavishly decorated china. These were set forth on a table laid with a cloth of lace or elaborately patterned satin damask. Their sheen was enhanced by the soft light of many candles, delicately shielded by shades of colored paper or cloth, like those shown on page 257.

The pampered hostesses of Miss Carter's book might select their tablewares from the fine shops in America's larger cities, or on their frequent trips abroad. The prosperous shopkeeper's or lawyer's wife in more isolated locations could, instead, depend on the mail order catalogs of importers and distributors like Higgins & Seiter. Besides, buying direct offered the thrifty the advantage of a 25% discount, a feature that Higgins & Seiter took pains to spell out in some detail.

Although their offerings included all sorts of novelties and decorative objects ranging from Sevres vases to stoneware steins to ceramic wall plaques, Higgins & Seiter stressed their extensive line of fine tablewares in glass and china. The featured glass was American, the china imported. This division in sources of supply had existed since before the Revolution.

As early as 1762, "Baron" Stiegel produced fine table glass, often decorated with engraving and rudimentary cutting. The other eighteenth-century glasshouse known to have made finely decorated wares was founded by John Frederick Amelung at New Bremen, Maryland, in 1784. Although neither of these factories survived the century, they had created a tradition of the domestic production of decorated glassware. It was probably workmen from Amelung, migrating westward, who manned the cutting shops of Bakewell and Page, founded in Pittsburgh in 1808. By 1825 at least four other glasshouses were turning out cut wares in the United States. With the decline of English glass cutting after 1850, American cut glass was generally acknowledged as the finest in the world. A set of Hawkes glass, cut in the Russian pattern, was made for the White House during the first administration of Grover Cleveland. When Theodore Roosevelt replenished the set, he lamented the fact that no American china of equal quality was available to complement it.

The President was only partially correct. By the time he took office, firms in Trenton, N. J. (notably Lenox, eventually the official source for White House china), and East Liverpool, Ohio, were producing porcelains of good quality. But it is true that up to the turn of the century most American attempts to make porcelain or bone china were abortive. Americans, therefore, from colonial times to the end of the Victorian era, set their tables with imported china. In the eighteenth and early nineteenth centuries, this was apt to be either English earthenware or Chinese porcelain. Although these continued to be popular throughout the period, the most fashionable wares towards the end of the century were English bone chine and French and German porcelains.

Higgins & Seiter was following a long tradition in offering its customers American glass and imported porcelains of high quality. American cut glass, in fact, had reached its peak when Higgins & Seiter published its 1899 catalog. This was the heart of the so-called "Brilliant Period," which most authorities date from 1880 to 1915.

American glass of the first half of the nineteenth century was based largely on English models, employing relatively simple straight-cut motifs. By the middle of the century, the popularity of cut glass had waned. Changing taste demanded more elaborate decoration; military needs during the Civil War preempted the use of lead, a necessary ingredient in the fine flint glass required for cutting; the economic panic of 1873 forced the closing of many independent cutting shops.

Widespread American interest in cut glass, as in so many of the decorative arts, was revived or aroused at the Philadelphia Centennial exhibition. In particular the display of Gillinder & Sons of Philadelphia, who set up a working cutting shop at the fair, commanded attention. A number of visitors to the centennial city carried home small pieces of cut glass as souvenirs. Among other companies producing cut glass at this time were the Mount Washington Glass Co., South Boston, Mass. (which became part of the Pairpoint Corp., c. 1895); the New England Glass Co., South Boston, Mass. (later taken over by Libbey and moved to Toledo, Ohio, in 1888); C. Dorflinger & Sons, Inc., White Mills, Penn.; and T. G. Hawkes & Co., Corning, N. Y.

By 1880 the use of new fuels had resulted in production of a heavy, very clear and brilliant glass adaptable to deep cutting. The perfection of the technique of making curved and deeply mitered cuts led to the creation of highly complex patterns. When a Hawkes dinner service, in the Grecian pattern, won the International Grand Prize at the Paris Exposition of 1889, American cut glass was acknowledged as the finest in the world.

By the turn of the century there were some eighty cutting shops in operation. Among the better known of this later group were J. D. Bergen, Meriden, Conn.; T. B. Clark & Co., Inc., Honesdale, Penn.; H. C. Fry Glass Co., Rochester, Penn. (after 1900); J. Hoare & Co., Corning, N. Y.; L. Straus & Sons, New York, N. Y.; Tuthill Cut Glass Co., Middletown, N. Y.

Many of these firms tried to protect their distinctive patterns by patenting them. These patent rights were difficult to enforce, however, and many firms copied one another's patterns, relying on minute variations to avoid suits. Knowledgeable collectors, therefore, judge a piece of cut glass not just by the pattern, but by the quality and brilliance of the glass, as well as the precision and depth with which the cutting was executed. The pictures in this catalog can, therefore, serve as a guide to certain patterns but cannot substitute for the examination and handling of an actual piece in making attributions. Collectors also depend on maker's marks etched into the glass. These marks were usually placed in inconspicuous spots, however, and may be elusive to the novice. Replicas of such marks will be found in several of the books listed in the bibliography.

Attribution of the various types of ceramic wares illustrated in the catalog is a relatively simple matter. By the turn of the century most reputable manufacturers marked their pieces very thoroughly. Not only the factory, but often the pattern name was included in the mark. Such factories as Minton and Wedgwood also used letters or other symbols to indicate the year of manufacture. In addition, after 1891 the United States required that the country of origin be included as part of the mark. Detailed descriptions and illustrations of these marks can be found in several of the books listed in the bibliography.

The lavish quality of hospitality at the turn of the century was reflected in the range and size of sets offered. Dinner sets were for twelve, but in addition to these, there were separate and distinctive sets made for serving fish, game, chops, oysters, ice cream and other desserts, tea, coffee and chocolate. Besides tablewares of all kinds, porcelains were also made in a variety of special shapes for use on the desk or dressing table.

The best, or at least the most expensive dinner services carried by Higgins & Seiter were English. For the most part, they were the products of firms that had attained eminence in the Victorian era. Atlhough Minton and Wedgwood were founded in the eighteenth century, the former gained its greatest renown after its entries at the Crystal Palace Exhibition of 1851 scored a triumph, climaxed by Queen Victoria's purchase of one of their displays, a dessert service. As for Wedgwood, although it made a small amount of bone china early in the nineteenth century, the line was dropped and not reintroduced until 1878. Doulton only added porcelains to its line of earthenwares a year earlier, in 1877. These firms, in contrast to those that had traditions of fine porcelain manufacture reaching back to the eighteenth century—Worcester, Derby and Coalport—catered particularly to the American market, producing special patterns for export.

Probably the most popular fine china in nineteenth-century America was produced in the French town of Limoges. It was made in numerous patterns of varying quality, so that the price range was wide. The Higgins & Seiter catalog lists sets ranging from $220.50, comparable in price to Wedgwood, down to $25, at which price it was competitive with English earthenwares. Part of the price differential was undoubtedly due to methods of decoration. In 1875 Limoges began to employ chrome-lithography (decalcomania), in addition to continuing hand-painting.

Although several factories operated at Limoges, the most famous were the several controlled by the Haviland family, which included that producing the "Elite" line. David Haviland, along with his brother Edmund, opened an importing business in New York City in 1834. In 1839 they began importing Limoges china, but while their customers liked the quality of the ware, they did not find the shapes or the decoration pleasing. Accordingly in 1842 David Haviland established his own factory at Limoges producing wares specially designed for the American market. Limoges china, a true porcelain, is thinner and more translucent than English bone china. Although it is also, therefore, somewhat more perishable, it was produced and imported in such enormous quantity that there is still a great deal of it available to collectors.

In the early 1900's Limoges' chief competition, at least in the moderate price range, was German and Austrian porcelain. At this time Germany was the second largest china-producing country in the world, surpassed only by England. Several of the factories, in particular those at Dresden (Meissen) and Vienna, had been turning out a fine, true porcelain since the early eighteenth century. While not comparable with the classic porcelains of the great period, their late nineteenth-century wares were of good quality. German porcelains, in general, were characterized by a very white, rather glassy paste. Speciments from individual locales can, of course, be distinguished by the marks, of which the best known are the crossed swords of Dresden and the beehive of Vienna.

Whether English, French or German, the china of the turn-of-the-century exhibited certain characteristics. Like most of the decorative arts of the Victorian era, in particular of the second half of the nineteenth century, it displayed a prediliction for the rich, curved forms derived from the Baroque and Rococo styles of the seventeenth and early eighteenth centuries. In china this was expressed in the shape of pieces, as well as in the decoration. Plates were not merely round; their edges were scalloped and indented. Holloware pieces swelled in and out in undulating curves.

The decoration, while lavish by modern standards, was restrained in comparison to the flamboyant wares of the 1850's to 80's. Gold was still heavily used, usually softened by burnishing or etching, especially on the more expensive pieces. But the floral motifs tended to be delicate, and small geometric designs were also popular. Colors were generally fairly soft.

Until about a decade ago, cut glass and late Victorian china were ignored by most dealers and serious collectors. Interest in these fields has been growing rapidly, and prices have risen accordingly. Nevertheless, in relation to their original cost, these wares may still be classified as a good buy. The cut glass employed a metal of remarkable clarity and brilliance, and the workmanship on many examples is superb. In porcelains, as well, the technical problems involved in the manufacture of paste and glazes, which add to the fascination of eighteenth and early nineteenth-century ceramics, had been solved. While the later wares may lack the individuality of some of the earlier designs, they have the virtue of exhibiting a uniformly high degree of technical proficiency. These late pieces are still sufficiently common so that the collector can afford to exercise a cautious selectivity. Catalogs such as this are extremely useful in assessing the relative initial value of the pieces offered.

Suggestions for further reading

on glass:

DANIEL, DOROTHY. *Cut and Engraved Glass.* New York: Barrows & Co., 1965. Reprint edition distributed by William Morrow & Co.

DANIEL, DOROTHY. *Price Guide to American Cut Glass.* New York: Barrows & Co., 1967. Distributed by William Morrow & Co.

DORFLINGER, WILLIAM F. "The Development of the Cut Glass Business in the United States." A paper read before the American Association of Flint and Lime Glass Manufacturers, at the annual meeting at Atlantic City, N. J., July 25, 1902.

MCCLINTOCK, KATHERINE MORRISON. *Collecting American Glass.* New York: Gramercy Publishing Co., 1950.

PEARSON, J. MICHAEL AND DOROTHY T. *American Cut Glass for the Discriminating Collector.* New York: Vantage Press, 1965.

PEARSON, J. MICHAEL AND DOROTHY T. *A Study of American Cut Glass Collections.* Miami, Fla.: The Franklin Press, 1969.

REVI, ALBERT CHRISTIAN. *American Cut and Engraved Glass.* New York: Thomas Nelson & Sons, 1964.

on china:

CUSHION, J. P. *German Ceramic Marks.* London: Faber and Faber, 1961. Issued by Boston Book and Art Shop, Boston, Mass., 1962.

GODDEN, GEOFFREY. *Victorian Porcelain.* New York: Thomas Nelson & Sons, 1961.

GODDEN, GEOFFREY. *Encyclopedia of British Pottery and Porcelain Marks.* New York, Bonanza Books., n.d.

HILLIER, BEVIS. *Pottery and Porcelain, 1700–1914.* New York: Meredith Press, 1968.

KOVEL, RALPH M. AND TERRY. *Dictionary of Marks—Pottery and Porcelain.* New York: Crown, 1953.

REYNOLDS, ERNEST. *Collecting Victorian Porcelain.* New York: Praeger, 1968.

WARE, GEORGE W. *German and Austrian Porcelain.* New York: Crown, 1963.

WOOD, SERRY. *Haviland-Limoges.* China Classics II. Watkins Glen, N. Y.: Century House, 1951.

Public collections of late nineteenth-century glass and china

The following public historical and art museums have indicated that they do have within their holdings pieces of Victorian cut glass and china. Some of the items will be found on permanent display, others are included in period rooms with other historical pieces, and yet others are displayed only when space allows.

Arizona Pioneers' Historical Museum, Tucson, Ariz.
Atlanta Historical Society, Atlanta, Ga.
Brooklyn Museum, Brooklyn, N. Y.
Brooks Memorial Art Gallery, Memphis, Tenn.
El Monte Historical Museum, El Monte, Calif.
Evansville Museum of Arts and Sciences, Evansville, Ind.
Fine Arts Gallery of San Diego, San Diego, Calif.
Florida State Museum, Gainesville, Fla.

Grand Rapids Public Museum, Grand Rapids, Mich.
Greensboro Historical Museum, Greensboro, N. C.
Henry Ford Museum and Greenfield Village, Dearborn, Mich.
Historical Museum and Institute of Western Colorado, Grand Junction, Colo.
Issac Delgado Museum of Art, New Orleans, La.
Kansas State Historical Society Museum, Topeka, Kans.
Lane County Pioneer Museum, Eugene, Ore.
Los Angeles County Museum of Art, Los Angeles, Calif.
Maryland Historical Society, Baltimore, Md.
Mattatuck Museum, Waterbury, Conn.
Metropolitan Museum, New York, N. Y.
Michigan Historical Commission Museum, Lansing, Mich.
Missouri Historical Society, St. Louis, Mo.
Museum of the City of Mobile, Mobile, Ala.
Museum of Fine Arts, Boston, Mass.
Nassau County Historical Museum, Syosset, N. Y.
Nebraska State Historical Society, Lincoln, Neb.
Nevada Historical Society, Reno, Nev.
New Jersey Historical Society, Newark, N. J.
New Jersey State Museum, Trenton, N. J.
Newark Museum, Newark, N. J.
New York Historical Society, New York, N. Y.
Oakland Museum, Oakland, Calif.
Old Court House Museum, Vicksburg, Miss.
Orange County Historical Museum, Orlando, Fla.
Pioneer Woman Museum, Ponca City, Okla.
R. W. Norton Art Gallery, Shreveport, La.
San Bernardino County Museum, Bloomington, Calif.
San Diego Historical Society, Serra Museum, San Diego, Calif.
Smithsonian Institution, Fine Arts Museum, Washington, D. C.
Wadsworth Atheneum, Hartford, Conn.
Western Reserve Historical Society Museum, Cleveland, Ohio
William Penn Memorial Museum, Harrisburg, Penn.
Witte Memorial Museum, San Antonio, Tex.